Also from Ann Silvers

"Silver Lining" Journals, Workbooks & Planners

Building Skills to Uplevel Life:
Emotional Intelligence Workbook

Learn, Let Go, Lighten Up:
Emotional Detox Journal and Workbook

Increasing My Happiness Quotient:
Joy Journal and Workbook

Roses, Thorns and Buds:
Journal for Daily Joys, Challenges and Inspirations

From To-Do to Ta-Done!
6-Month Daily To-Do List Planner

Books

Feed Your Calm: Anti-Anxiety Anti-Stress Diet and Supplement Tips for Stress Resilience

A quick look at Anxiety:
Simple Powerful Anti-Anxiety Tips
for Stress, Anxiety, and Panic Attack Relief

Hypnosis Recordings

Hypnosis can be very helpful for relaxation, sleep, releasing emotional pain, and improving how you deal with stress. My *Release and Refresh Emotional Detox Hypnosis* helps you let go of anything that has burdened, stressed, or overwhelmed you. My *Discover Calm Anti-Anxiety Hypnosis* reinforces 5 relaxation skills that I teach in this workbook and helps reduce overall anxiety. You can listen to either recording any time you have a half-hour to relax or as you are going to sleep.

Visit annsilvers.com often for the ever-expanding list of self-help products.

BECOMING CALM

Silver Lining
Anxiety and Stress Resilience
Workbook & Journal

Ann Silvers, MA

SILVERSPUBLISHING

ISBN: 978-1-948551-08-3

Printed in the United States of America

Published by Silvers Publishing, LLC
Gig Harbor, Washington, USA
www.silverspublishing.com
Contact the author at annsilvers.com.

Contents

Part Seven: Stress Resilience Lifestyle · 151

Part Eight: Calming Activity Pages · 181

Preface

I know how bad anxiety feels and how much it gets in the way of happiness because I've lived with anxiety myself. Before becoming a counselor, I stumbled along trying various ways to deal with my anxiety with limited results. Now, anxiety is no longer part of my everyday life. On the rare occasion that it rears its ugly head, I have an extensive anti-anxiety tool kit to draw from to put it in check.

This inside look at anxiety, coupled with what I've discovered about what works and doesn't work for counseling clients while helping them overcome everything from generalized anxiety to fear of flying to PTSD, has given me unique insight into what anxiety feels like, what relieves it, and what bolsters stress resilience.

Becoming Calm brings together what I've learned and closely recreates the step-by-step process I take clients through during a series of counseling sessions: starting with information about emotions in general and anxiety specifically, then moving into anti-anxiety skills, techniques, and tips.

I'm excited to present this material in workbook format. Workbooks allow for you to be given small bite-sized pieces of information and then immediate opportunities to use that information in an exercise before moving on to the next piece. It makes the information much more digestible than when it is presented in a book with one subject quickly following another.

Wishing you a calm, happy life,

-Ann Silvers

P.S.: I've obtained many advanced certifications since graduating with my Master's Degree in Counseling (MA). Those that are most relevant to my work with anxiety and the contents of this workbook include:

- Clinical Anxiety Treatment,
- Applying Neuroscience for the Treatment of Trauma, Anxiety, and Stress,
- Hypnotherapy, and
- Integrative Medicine for Mental Health.

Introduction

"Anxiety is a lot like a toddler.
It never stops talking,
tells you you're wrong about everything,
and wakes you up at 3 am."

—Author Unknown

Anxiety can suck the life out of life. It is draining, distracting, and debilitating. It revs you up and wears you out. It can make you immobile, irritable, and irrational. It can interfere with your job performance, reduce your quality of life, and undermine your relationships.

Anxiety ranges in intensity from a stressed-out overwhelmed feeling to a panic attack that sends you to the emergency room for a heart check. Different types of anxiety include:

- Generalized anxiety (GAD)
- Panic
- Social anxiety
- Phobias such as fear of flying
- Obsessive-compulsive disorder (OCD)
- Post-traumatic stress disorder (PTSD)

Anxiety is often found in combination with other mental challenges, such as depression.

If you have anxiety now or have experienced it in the past, you are not alone. The National Institute of Mental Health estimates that approximately one third (1 in 3) of American adults and teens experience anxiety in some form.

Sources of stress are going to be part of your life. You are going to be running late sometimes. You are going to have disagreements with people. You are going to have deadlines, whether it is getting dinner before baseball practice or transporting a kidney before it expires. The level of stress you experience in response to each of these threats is determined by your mental and physical state. Managing stress so that it doesn't turn into anxiety requires stress resilience: the ability to withstand stress, recover quickly, and spring back into shape.

Anxiety is emotional and physical

Anxiety is both emotional and physical. You feel the emotion of anxiety, and you feel the physical sensation of being anxious. Your body and mind are connected, and each affects the other: your biochemistry can alter your mood, and your mood can alter your biochemistry.

Anxiety is heightened fear. When fear provokes the fight, flight, or freeze response, it commands your body to perform specific chemical processes that are meant to keep you safe in times of danger. Some of the resulting physical changes are felt as the symptoms of anxiety.

Anxiety's physical manifestations are different for different people. One person might sweat, another person might have diarrhea, another constipation. Your particular body and the intensity of your anxiety will determine your symptoms.

There is an overlap between what is commonly called "anxiety" and what is labeled "panic," with panic being more mentally and physically intense.

Anxiety can last for long periods (days, weeks, months, or years) with symptoms that are sometimes better and worse. It can come over you slowly or quickly, stimulated by situations or thoughts, or it can be in the background most of the time.

Panic attacks appear suddenly with a surge of symptoms that usually peak within ten minutes. While they range in duration from seconds to hours, they typically subside within a half hour. Some people with anxiety never experience a panic attack, while others may have had years of anxiety peppered with a few or many panic episodes.

Anxiety may have any of the following physical symptoms. (Check those that apply for you.)

❑ Difficulty thinking

❑ Brain fog

❑ Headaches/migraines

❑ Trouble sleeping

❑ Skin rashes or hives

❑ Sweating

❑ Trembling or shaking

❑ Crackling or unsteady voice

❑ Dry mouth

❑ Tightness in the throat

❑ Increased heart rate

❑ Nausea or stomach upset

❑ Intestinal problems (gas, cramps, diarrhea, constipation, bloating, Irritable Bowel Syndrome)

Anxiety that has reached **panic** levels may have any of the symptoms listed above plus any of the following more intense symptoms. (Check those that apply for you.)

❑ Dizziness or faintness

❑ Chills or hot flushes

❑ Racing heart, palpitations, or chest pain

❑ Vision changes

❑ Numbness or tingling

❑ Shortness of breath

❑ Hyperventilation

❑ Difficulty moving

❑ Choking sensation

❑ Feeling detached from yourself or from reality

❑ Fear that you are losing control or dying

Panic attacks can feel like you are having a heart attack or are dying. I've experienced a couple of panic attacks myself. With the second one, I was so worried that I was going to pass out that I laid myself down on the floor, so if I passed out, I had nowhere to fall.

About Becoming Calm

The first half of *Becoming Calm* helps you figure out why you feel anxious. The second half gives you tools to reduce your anxiety and build stress resilience.

Becoming Calm is divided into eight parts:

1. **Understanding Emotions**

    Anxiety is in the fear family of emotions. The first steps toward understanding anxiety involve learning about emotions in general and fear specifically.

2. **Why You Feel What You Feel**

    The chapters in Part Two walk you through using the "I" message formula to uncover what's driving your anxiety.

3. **Journaling Pages**

    This part provides opportunities to use emotion-processing skills introduced in Parts One and Two. The journaling pages include prompts to guide your writing about times you currently feel anxious or have felt anxious in the past. Begin using these pages while you continue to work on Parts Four through Eight of the workbook.

4. **How to Relax & Reset**

    These 5 relaxation techniques and 5 quick reset grounding techniques can help counter the wound-up feeling that accompanies anxiety.

5. **Challenging Cognitive Distortions**

    Several common distorted ways of thinking contribute to anxious overreactions. Learning what cognitive distortions might be revving you up—and how to catch, check, and change them—has the potential to alleviate your anxiety.

6. **Anxiety-Reducing Mindset**

    These chapters can help shift your mindset away from anxiety-provoking approaches to life and toward anxiety-reducing ways of looking at things.

7. **Stress Resilience Lifestyle**

    Here I cover dietary habits that might be contributing to your anxiety and those that could help you become more stress resilient, as well as other anti-anxiety lifestyle tips.

8. **Calming Activity Pages**

    While the anti-anxiety benefits of these activity pages are explained in Chapter 65, near the end of Part Seven, you don't have to wait to venture into this section and enjoy the activities: an inspiring story, calming coloring pages, word games, and a maze. Dive into them whenever you like.

There are also lined pages at the back of the workbook for additional writing. Use these as overflow if you have more to say for any of the exercises or other thoughts.

How to use this workbook

Each person who uses this workbook has their own unique needs, challenges, goals, and ways they learn. Here are some considerations for getting the most out of *Becoming Calm*.

1. Begin by familiarizing yourself with the book's structure and content. Take a quick look through the chapters to get an overview of the material.

2. The book is designed with short chapters to break the learning into digestible chunks. It's OK to do multiple chapters at a time, but it's not a race; pace yourself so information can sink in and new skills can be practiced and strengthened before adding the next piece.

3. This is a workbook, but it is not like school homework. You get to decide how to use it.

    *   Allow yourself the freedom to modify or skip exercises that aren't a good fit for you.

    *   If an exercise frustrates you, don't let it stall you out. Find something else that is a better fit at that time. You may want to return to it later, or not. Either way, it's OK.

4. There are some considerations to the order you go through the workbook:

    *   The book is structured to build knowledge and skills as you move through the sections, but the further along in the book you go, the less this is relevant.

    *   Part Seven is a stand-alone in that the content is about lifestyle rather than anxiety knowledge and skills. You can put some of these tips into action while you work through other parts of the book.

    *   Identify sections or exercises that resonate with you the most and prioritize them. This allows you to address the areas that are most relevant or require immediate attention. (For example, you may benefit from the relaxation techniques found in Part Four as you work on other sections of the workbook.)

    *   By-passing some chapters to focus on later sections doesn't mean they are abandoned forever. You can return to them at a later date if you like.

    *   See my comments on the previous page about Part Three's journaling pages and Part Eight activities.

You can use this book on your own or as a complement to counseling. If any of the exercises trigger disturbing emotions, I encourage you to speak to a trusted friend and seek professional help if needed. Chapter 65 includes tips for reaching out for support, and Chapter 66 explains therapy options. If you need immediate help call your local/national suicide helpline. In the US call 988 for mental health crisis help.

Part One

Understanding Emotions

"When awareness is brought to an emotion,
power is brought to your life."

—Tara Meyer Robson

Anxiety is an emotion. Before we talk about this emotion specifically, let's first talk about emotions in general.

Emotions are information. They are like your own personal radar system, going out and bringing back pings of information.

The better you are at labeling your emotions and processing the information they have to offer, the better your life is.

Getting clear about what emotions you are feeling, and why you are feeling them, can help you make decisions that make your life better and better.

Examples of information in emotions

The information in fear: There is danger to myself or others.

The information in guilt: I did something that was harmful to myself, someone, or something.

The information in feeling respected: This is a good person for me to be around.

Ignorance is not bliss

Ignoring the information in emotions gets us in trouble.

When you don't deal with uncomfortable emotions directly, not only do you miss out on the information they have to offer, but you set yourself up in many negative ways.

Fear of big trucks on the move can keep you from walking out into the street as one passes by. Ignoring that feeling can be deadly. On the other hand, overreacting to that healthy fear could result in anxiety at the thought of walking on a sidewalk and get in the way of happiness.

When we don't deal with uncomfortable emotions directly, they tend to spill out in overreactions or anger. They can fester into depression. They fuel anxiety, nervousness, and worry. They can create unconscious drives that push addictions to food, substances, and unhealthy behaviors.

Here's an analogy that provides a concrete way of understanding emotions.

It's as if we have containers for each emotion inside of us: a container for fear, one for guilt, another for feeling loved, and so on. Different situations that stimulate a particular emotion add to the contents of that emotion's container.

Processing and retaining the information that each emotion has to offer adds to the structure of the emotion's container. In that way, year after year, you make the container structure stronger. (This parallels building emotional intelligence.)

Each container has a release valve at the bottom. When the system is working well,

- the emotion comes in,

- you gather the wisdom and understanding it has to offer,

- then you open the valve and the rest of the emotion flows out.

You can think of it as catch and release.

Even when the system is working well, a container might get pretty full for a while when a big emotionally-charged event happens, but processing the emotion through eventually makes room for the next situations that create that emotion.

Locking in the pain

I've just described the ideal scenario for feeling and using emotions. But that isn't what's happening for most people. For most people, the release valves on the containers for uncomfortable or painful emotions are all crazy-glued shut. And some people add the equivalent of locks and chains and cement: anything to keep from acknowledging and directly expressing some or all of the "negative" emotions.

It may be that they don't know how to deal with emotional pain, or they have been told that it's bad to have emotions, or there was a price to pay for expressing emotions, or the emotions are overwhelming. Whatever the reason, the release valves are sealed shut.

When a container is sealed shut, it isn't a flowing system like it's meant to be. It's a backing-up system. The container fills up, fast or slow, until it can't hold any more, and a seal or scum is created on top.

The next event that triggers that emotion breaks the seal and the pressurized emotion comes bursting out. The person doesn't feel just the emotion that was created by the current situation; they feel the storehouse of emotion. The stored emotion explodes out, creating overreactions, blurted responses, anger, and/or depression.

It could be a big emotional event that punctures the seal, or it could be a very small emotional event. It could be so small that it is just a hint of the possibility that someone is going to treat you in a way that could create that emotion. When an emotion container is full and locked, even a pinprick's worth of emotion is enough to break the container's seal and create an overwhelming burst of emotional pain.

When you know how to open the emotion release valves, you have conscious control of your emotions and behaviors. When you ignore your uncomfortable emotions or don't know how to process them, they take control without you being consciously aware of what they are up to.

Reflect on the containers of emotion concept.

Do you recognize yourself or others in this explanation of emotions? In what way?

What messages did you receive about expressing "negative" emotions as a child?

Have you had relationships where there was a price to pay for expressing emotional pain?

3. Overreactions

Emotional overreactions are more emotion than the amount warranted by whatever just happened. Overreactions are one of the side effects of having stored uncomfortable emotions.

Overreactions occur when a current event breaks the seal of stored emotion and you feel not only the emotion that goes with what just happened—you also feel a whole lot of stored emotion. It can stimulate a small burst of overreaction or a torrent.

Sometimes emotional overreactions are outward and dramatic; sometimes they are barely visible to the outside world but pack an inner punch.

A person having an overreaction can mistakenly think that all the emotion they are feeling is about what just happened. They can then conclude what just happened "must be terrible!" because it caused all this pain. And they may think that whoever else was involved "must be terrible!" because they caused all this pain. In reality, the amount of emotion isn't only about what just happened; it's also about the emotional accumulation from old events.

One of the challenges with overreactions is to determine how much of the emotional response is directly connected to what just happened. The answer to that question can be anywhere from "nearly nothing" to "most of it."

Reflection. Describe a time you overreacted.

Scale your overreaction. How much of the emotional pain that you felt at the time do you think was really about what happened and how much was about something else?

0%   **OVERREACTION SCALE**   100%

0% = all the emotion was about the triggering event. 100% = none of the emotion was about the triggering event. (It's never going to be 100% overreaction, but sometimes it can be very close.)

12

2 sources of overreactions

There are two sources of emotional overreactions:

1. Direct Hit
2. Add-On

1. Direct Hit

An overreaction can occur because a filled-to-the-brim storehouse of emotion just took a direct hit.

For example: If your feeling-disrespected container is full, new experiences of feeling disrespected will break into that stored emotion. It may be that someone really is disrespecting you now, or it may be just the hint of the possibility that you could be disrespected. Either way, it breaks the seal on the full container and results in a bigger emotional response than what is warranted by current events.

2. Add-On

An overreaction can also occur from an overwhelming mixture of emotions.

To further use the containers analogy: The containers are connected to one another, and there are spillways that can release pressure from one container into another when multiple emotions are stimulated around the same time.

When an emotion container that a spillway dumps into can't handle anything more, it bursts its seal and creates an overreaction. With emotional add-on, we may mistakenly think that whatever happened last caused all the pain and that all the pain is associated with the one emotion that's bursting.

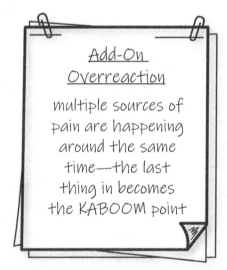

Direct Hit
Overreaction

emotion from a
current event taps
into a full
container of
old emotional
pain/discomfort

Add-On
Overreaction

multiple sources of
pain are happening
around the same
time—the last
thing in becomes
the KABOOM point

Feeling powerless at work, adds to fear of being late, adds to frustration that the cap got left off the toothpaste. You find yourself screaming at the toothpaste culprit or suddenly drenched in tears. The amount of emotional pain felt isn't just from frustration over the toothpaste.

> **Direct Hit or Add-On?** For the overreaction you described on the previous page, check the box for whether your overreaction was a Direct Hit tapping into that same emotion from another time, or an Add-On doubling or tripling up with other sources of emotional discomfort around the same time.

❑ Direct Hit   ❑ Add-On

4. The Anger Ooze

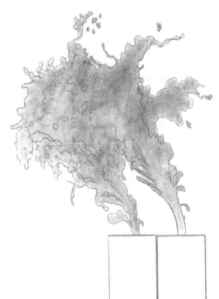

Some of the overflow from the painful emotion containers collects in what I call the *Anger Ooze*.

Anger is a secondary emotion. Some sort of emotional pain or discomfort (fear, rejection, shame . . .) isn't getting dealt with directly and is being turned into anger.

Anger is an energy that seems to demand release. It acts like a heat-seeking missile looking for a target. It may create small to large outward explosions, ranging from irritated tone or biting sarcasm to rage. Or, it may implode, causing a drive to numb out, leading to depression or addictive behaviors.

There is some relief of pressure when anger is released, but other emotion containers may still be filled to the brim, on the verge of bursting, or the emotion container that overflowed can easily burst again the next time that emotion is experienced. In either case, the Anger Ooze grows again and seeks another release opportunity.

Anger begs the question, "What emotional discomfort isn't getting dealt with directly and is getting turned into anger?" It may be one emotion or many.

Given that depression may be anger turned inwards, a similar question can be asked when depressed, "What's in my emotion containers that is creating this depression?" With addictions, the question is, "What's in my emotion containers that I am trying to numb out?"

Reflection. You and anger.

Does your anxiety sometimes come out as anger?

Does it contribute to depression?

Does it create a drive toward unhealthy numbing out behaviors?

5. Losing that Feel-Good Feeling

Ignored "negative" emotions seem determined to hang around until they get to do their job of giving information. Ignored "positive" emotions, on the other hand, don't seem to wait on our attention.

Lack of attention to positive emotions is the equivalent of having the feel-good emotion container release valves stuck in the open position. When the release valves are stuck open, the emotions just whoosh on through without there being a chance to grab the information they have to offer and keep that information. Compliments aren't absorbed. Love isn't felt. Your own accomplishments go unnoticed.

Having the release valves stuck open is the equivalent of emotional diarrhea. It leaves you feeling emotionally malnourished.

Ignored positive emotions that stream through without recognition leave a void. That void can contribute to depression and create unconscious drives to fill up the emptiness with unhealthy sources of happiness, while the healthy sources of happiness go unnoticed. The void contributes to anxiety because anxiety-balancing emotions, like feeling secure, aren't retained. It leaves you with no chips in the bank to deal with stress.

With feel-good emotions, it's important to learn to close the release valves long enough to actually feel the emotion, gather the information the emotion has to offer, and retain the feel-good feeling. The information in feel-good emotions includes:

- what led to happiness,
- whether the source of the happiness is good for you, and
- why you are drawn to certain things.

Discovering healthy sources of happiness can lead you to figure out how to get more of that in your life. Discovering unhealthy sources of happiness can lead you to figure out what pulls or pushes you toward that source, and how to make changes to free you from that draw.

Reflection. You and feel-good emotions.

How are you at retaining feel-good emotions?

6. Reality and Fantasy

Emotions are stimulated by both reality and fantasy.

We respond to a scary movie with fear even though we're outsiders looking at what we know isn't a real occurrence. We can break out in a sweat just thinking about giving a speech. We can become angry imagining someone said something hurtful intentionally, whether or not it is the truth of the matter. And that anger can grow and grow as we play it over and over.

With anxiety, our mind tends to go around in circles as we think about awful stuff. We'll talk more about how to stop that ruminating later. For now, just be aware that you will have the same emotional response to something that you vividly imagine as you do to something that is real.

Reflection. Reality or imaginary?

How much of your anxiety is based in reality and how much is from imagined scenarios?

Do you tend to ruminate: vividly thinking awful thoughts over and over?

Describe a time when your anxiety was about something you imagined happening.

_____

_____

_____

_____

_____

_____

_____

7. Expanding Your Emotion Vocabulary

When it comes to emotions, people tend to be taught what I call *The Famous Four: mad, glad, sad*, and *afraid*.

There are thousands of emotion words in the English language. Only knowing four is very limiting. It creates an emotional handicap that gets in the way of understanding what's going on for yourself and for others.

Notice that only one of the four—*glad*—is for anything feel-good. I believe that this contributes to our lack of recognition and savoring of feel-good emotions.

One of the four emotions is *mad*. I think that this contributes to the frequency of emotional pain being expressed as anger or felt as depression (anger turned inwards).

And one of the four is *afraid*. This overgeneralization of emotional pain makes for all emotions that have an element of fear (and many do) being clumped together. I think that this contributes to the epidemic of anxiety.

My 101 Emotions list

The next page contains the list of 101 emotions that I created while working with individuals, couples, and groups, to help people build their emotion vocabulary.

This list isn't all the emotion words that could be on a list, but it's a good step up from four.

The emotions on the list are divided into comfortable and uncomfortable. I worked for years to figure out what to call them besides positive and negative, because those labels too easily leave the impression that some emotions are good and some are bad.

Surprised appears on both lists as an example that not all emotions fit neatly into one or the other category. There are welcomed surprises and unwelcomed surprises.

Angry appears in parentheses on the uncomfortable list because it is a secondary emotion. There is some kind of emotional pain or discomfort underneath the anger that is not getting dealt with directly. With any level of anger, from mild irritation to rage, the question is "What's underneath this anger?" For any one anger event, there might be one emotion underneath or many.

Having not only *mad, glad, sad*, and *afraid* but also labels like *disappointed, frustrated, resentful, relieved, and appreciated* available greatly improves your understanding of yourself and others.

8. 101 Emotions List

COMFORTABLE EMOTIONS

Accepted	Confident	Excited	Liberated	Safe
Acknowledged	Connected	Exhilarated	Loved	Satisfied
Amused	Considered	Grateful	Nurtured	Secure
Appreciated	Content	Happy	Passionate	Stimulated
Attracted	Creative	Hopeful	Protected	Supported
Attractive	Curious	Important	Proud	Surprised*
Calm	Delighted	Included	Reassured	Trusted
Capable	Empowered	Independent	Relaxed	Trusting
Caring	Encouraged	Inspired	Relieved	Understood
Competent	Enthusiastic	Interested	Respected	Valued
				Welcome

UNCOMFORTABLE EMOTIONS

Abandoned	Defeated	Foolish	Manipulated	Resentful
Afraid	Defensive	Frustrated	Nervous	Sad
(Angry)**	Devastated	Grief	Obligated	Shame
Anxious	Disappointed	Guilty	Offended	Shocked
Belittled	Disconnected	Humiliated	Overwhelmed	Surprised*
Betrayed	Discounted	Inadequate	Panic	Trapped
Concerned	Discouraged	Inferior	Powerless	Unappreciated
Confused	Disrespected	Insecure	Pressured	Unattractive
Controlled	Embarrassed	Jealous	Regret	Violated
Deceived	Excluded	Lonely	Rejected	Vulnerable
				Worried

* Surprised is an example of an emotion that is sometimes comfortable and sometimes uncomfortable.

** Angry is a secondary emotion: some other uncomfortable emotion(s) is/are under the anger.

9. Recognizing Your Emotions

Practice identifying comfortable emotions. Pick any comfortable emotion and write about a time you felt that emotion.

Practice identifying uncomfortable emotions. Pick any uncomfortable emotion and write about a time you felt that emotion.

10. More Than One at a Time

Situations can stimulate more than one emotion. Sometimes those emotions are similar to one another, other times diametrically opposed to each other. Sometimes they balance each other.

It's important that you acknowledge (at least to yourself) the full range of what you're feeling.

Situation #1: Getting corrective advice at work

You might feel angry if someone at work points out that you should or could improve on something. Under the anger, there might be many uncomfortable emotions, such as feeling unappreciated, incompetent, humiliated, guilty, discouraged, insecure, nervous, rejected, and resentful.

Situation #2: Moving

You can be excited about a move, happy about the new job you're moving to, and relieved that more money will be coming in; at the same time, you can grieve the loss of contact with friends and family, familiar surroundings, and elements of the job you're leaving behind.

> **Reflection.** Can you think of a time you felt stressed out in a situation when you had more than one uncomfortable feeling going on at once? Write about that situation, including naming the emotions involved.

11. The Fear Family of Emotions

Some emotions are very similar to each other. Several words on the 101 list, including anxiety, describe different levels of fear. Anxiety is a member of what I call the fear family of emotions. Other members of the fear family include panic, nervousness, worry, and concern. Any of them may be felt as, or labeled as, *stress*.

Some people find it relatively easy to acknowledge that they feel stressed, but are uncomfortable with the idea that fear is behind that feeling. They don't identify with the concept of being afraid. If you are one of those people, hang in there with me on this. Humor me a bit and maybe you'll get a different understanding about fear.

As I said earlier, all emotions are information. The information in fear is "danger": "danger to myself, someone, or something." Fear's job then, is to warn us of danger. It is a natural part of our experience as a human being (actually, as an animal as well). It is there for our survival. It's meant to keep us safe. That's great when there really is danger and the amount of fear felt is proportional to what stimulated the fear.

Fear's message: "Danger!"

Some fears are rational—they are a healthy level of fear based on reality.

Listening to the information in fear can keep you safe:

- ☑ Fearing the physical pain and damage that could come from touching a hot stove keeps you from touching a hot stove.
- ☑ Fear of regret can keep you from doing something that goes against your values.
- ☑ Fearing growing old can stimulate you to exercise and eat well to maximize your health as you age.

Some fears are not so rational or logical. They are overreactions driven by subconscious connections that you aren't able to consciously understand or control. Fear that is an overreaction fuels persistent debilitating feelings of anxiety, nervousness, worry, and stress, or incapacitating spikes of those emotions or of panic.

Very few things are true emergencies, but a fear overreaction can cause simple things to feel like an emergency. Worry over how someone filled the dishwasher "wrong" becomes an emergency equivalent to there being a lion at the gate.

What we want to be able to do with fear is to be logical. We want to think through what we are afraid of, how much of the fear is really about now, how much is an overreaction, and what we want to do in response to the fear. We'll talk lots about how to get to that rational place and tools for staying there in later sections, but for now, we need to explore the concepts of fear a bit more.

12. The Fear Hierarchy

Panic, anxiety, nervousness, worry, and concern are all in the fear family of emotions. They are different degrees of fear intensity. Any of them can be felt as "stress." (Note: some people feel all the levels of fear, some experience a few of the levels, and some tend to spend a lot of time on one particular level.) The hierarchy of fear:

↓ decreasing intensity

PANIC
ANXIETY
NERVOUSNESS / WORRY
CONCERN
_____
OBLIVIOUS / NUMB

As you think about the fear hierarchy, keep in mind that what you need to be able to do with fear is to be logical. Ideally, you can logically think through what you are afraid of, how much of the fear is really about now, how much is an overreaction, and what you want to do in response to the fear.

The higher on the hierarchy your fear level, the more energy you burn up and the less you are able to think clearly:

→ **At the level of panic,** fear is immobilizing. You have trouble breathing, let alone accomplishing other tasks. You are focused on staying alive. Your brain can't think clearly.

→ **Anxiety** consumes your physical, mental, and emotional energy. There is a tendency to fixate on negative subjects and think in circles. It's difficult to constructively focus your mind.

→ **Nervousness and worry** create a slow burn in the background. They drain energy and distract the mind, making it difficult to clearly think through options and take constructive action.

→ **Concern** is the sweet spot. Concern can be energizing. It allows you to get direction. It tells you something is important and in need of your attention. You can clearly think through, "Is this something I should really be afraid of because there is danger to myself or others, or am I overreacting?" At concern, you can think through your options and decide on the best course of action.

→ **Oblivious** is the numbed-out position. Here there is an avoidance of the fear. People can get to oblivious by having an inner coping mechanism of going numb, by using substances to zone out, or by ignoring a problem (the "ignorance is bliss" philosophy).

Many people consciously or subconsciously think that oblivious is the desired condition. When they feel the higher levels of fear—panic, anxiety, nervousness, worry—they may think that going oblivious or numb is the goal. It is not. It's OK to calm and distract yourself for a little while, but oblivious is a dangerous place to stay.

Concern is the goal. At the level of concern, you can calmly work with the fear and use it as part of your emotional feedback system. Concern can help make your life better.

decreasing intensity

PANIC (immobilizing)
ANXIETY (consuming)
NERVOUSNESS / WORRY (distracting)
CONCERN *the sweet spot
_____
OBLIVIOUS / NUMB (avoiding)

When you experience the more intense levels of fear, you can benefit from learning how to lower your emotional response down to the level of concern. I'll give you many ways to reduce panic, anxiety, nervousness, and worry down to concern in later sections. Before we do that, there are a few more pieces to learn about fear.

Reflection. What are your takeaways from this section?

---

13. Feared Things

People experience a wide range of fears over things big and small, within and outside of their control. Some fears are rational and helpful protection. Some are overreactions that get in the way of health and happiness.

Here are some potential fears. Check those that apply to you and add others that you experience. Mark the R check box for fears that you experience at Rational levels (warranted and at reasonable levels). Mark the I/O check box for those things you tend to have Irrational/Overreaction fear levels for.

R	I/O	FEARED THING
☐	☐	touching a hot stove
☐	☐	running out in front of a moving truck
☐	☐	not getting to watch a favorite TV show
☐	☐	not making the mortgage payment
☐	☐	losing a job
☐	☐	growing old
☐	☐	imperfection
☐	☐	change
☐	☐	public speaking
☐	☐	taking a test
☐	☐	failing
☐	☐	succeeding
☐	☐	loss of control
☐	☐	dying
☐	☐	flying
☐	☐	the toothpaste drying out
☐	☐	getting hurt (physically, emotionally, spiritually, financially, sexually...)
☐	☐	the dishwasher not getting filled "right"
☐	☐	
☐	☐	
☐	☐	
☐	☐	
☐	☐	

14. Fear of the Fear

An important common fear for people who have experienced panic, or have chronic anxiety, nervousness, or worry, is fear of the fear.

It is common to get anxious about the possibility of getting anxious.

Here are some examples:

- **People who are burdened by not being able to sleep because of anxiety** can get anxious about the anxiety itself. At the first signs of anxiety, they become worried that the anxiety will keep them from sleeping. The worry about the anxiety makes the anxiety grow bigger.

- **People who have experienced a panic attack in the past** often avoid situations similar to those that stimulated the panic initially out of fear that they will have another attack.

- **People who have had negative experiences from being nervous** often get nervous that they will get nervous in a situation that has caused that response in the past.

Clients often feel relieved when I tell them that these are common feelings that accompany anxiety, nervousness, worry, and panic. If you feel relieved by hearing this, take a minute to savor the relief of knowing that you are not alone in this.

> **Reflection.** Write about your experiences with fear of the fear, getting nervous about the possibility of getting nervous, or anxious about the possibility of being anxious, etc. How does it control your life? How do you deal with it?

15. The Fear Connection

Besides emotions such as anxiety, nervousness, worry, concern, and panic, that are directly indicative of varying degrees of fear, fear is connected to emotional pain in three ways:

1. Mislabeling emotional pain as "afraid"
2. Fear behind the pain
3. Fear of the pain

1. Mislabeling emotional pain as "afraid"

The tendency to lump all emotions into *The Famous Four: mad, glad, sad, and afraid* can result in a wide range of emotions being experienced as "afraid."

Feeling rejected, or obligated, or disrespected, for example, may have an element of fear, but the information in the emotion is more usable when the emotion is labeled more precisely.

2. Fear behind the pain

There can be an element of fear in many painful or uncomfortable emotions. Labeling a particular emotion can point to a connected fear. Here are some examples of emotions and possible connected fears:

abandoned ➡ fear that you are alone, fear that someone doesn't want to be with you

shame ➡ fear that someone won't like you, fear that you are deeply flawed

controlled ➡ fear that you don't have control yourself, fear that you're being forced to do something you don't want to do

> **What might the fears be behind these emotions?** Fill in the fears related to these emotions and check completed emotion words off the list on the next page. (There are many possible answers. Use whatever comes to mind for you.)

trapped ➡ fear that _____

embarrassed ➡ fear that _____

defensive ➡ fear that _____

obligated ➤ fear that _____

manipulated ➤ fear that _____

lonely ➤ fear that _____

defeated ➤ fear that _____

insecure ➤ fear that _____

belittled ➤ fear that _____

guilty ➤ fear that _____

powerless ➤ fear that _____

jealous ➤ fear that _____

betrayed ➤ fear that _____

discouraged ➤ fear that _____

_____ ➤ fear that _____
(Pick an unchecked
emotion from the list.)

☑ Abandoned
☐ Afraid
☐ Angry (secondary)
☐ Anxious
☐ Belittled
☐ Betrayed
☐ Concerned
☐ Confused
☑ Controlled
☐ Deceived
☐ Defeated
☐ Defensive
☐ Devastated
☐ Disappointed
☐ Disconnected
☐ Discounted
☐ Discouraged
☐ Disrespected
☐ Embarrassed
☐ Excluded
☐ Foolish
☐ Frustrated
☐ Grief
☐ Guilty
☐ Humiliated
☐ Inadequate
☐ Inferior
☐ Insecure
☐ Jealous
☐ Lonely
☐ Manipulated
☐ Nervous
☐ Obligated
☐ Offended
☐ Overwhelmed
☐ Panic
☐ Powerless
☐ Pressured
☐ Regret
☐ Rejected
☐ Resentful
☐ Sad
☑ Shame
☐ Shocked
☐ Surprised
☐ Trapped
☐ Unappreciated
☐ Unattractive
☐ Violated
☐ Vulnerable
☐ Worried

27

3. Fear of the pain

Fear warns us of potential harm. Potential harm can be physical, financial, emotional, psychological, sexual, or spiritual. The harm done could be to yourself, someone, or something.

Healthy fear of emotional pain can serve to keep you from doing harm to yourself or others. For example:

- ☑ Fear of shame can keep you from doing something that goes against your values.
- ☑ Fear of being controlled can empower you to stay out of relationships with controlling people.

Unhealthy fear of emotional pain occurs when you don't know how to deal with emotional pain in a skillful way. That lack of skill can wreak havoc. For example:

- ☒ An unhealthy fear of shame can keep you from living your life to the fullest—or to any level of satisfaction.
- ☒ An unhealthy fear of being controlled can drive you to be controlling yourself or overreact to someone voicing a differing opinion of how things could be done.

Reflection. How does healthy fear of emotional pain help you?

Reflection. How does unhealthy fear of emotional pain cause trouble for you?

1. Emotions are information. They are created by both reality and fantasy. You can feel more than one emotion at a time. Those emotions may even be opposites. There's value in expanding your emotion vocabulary beyond *The Famous Four: mad, glad, sad,* and *afraid.*

2. Unprocessed painful emotions don't go away. They get stored. Stored painful emotions cause overreactions when they get tapped into. Overreactions are from a Direct Hit into the container of that same emotion, or an Add-On to other emotions.

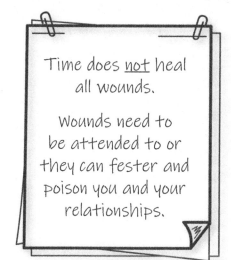

Time does <u>not</u> heal all wounds.

Wounds need to be attended to or they can fester and poison you and your relationships.

3. Anger is a secondary emotion. There is some sort of emotional pain that isn't getting dealt with directly and is being turned into anger.

4. Fear's message is "danger": "danger to myself, someone, or something." There is a fear family of emotions that form a hierarchy of fear from more intense to less intense:

decreasing intensity

PANIC (immobilizing)
ANXIETY (consuming)
NERVOUSNESS / WORRY (distracting)
CONCERN *the sweet spot
—————————————————
OBLIVIOUS / NUMB (avoiding)

Concern is the fear sweat spot. At concern you can be logical. You can question what is causing the fear, consider options, and make a plan of action. Some people try to avoid fear by going to an oblivious/numb place.

5. Some fears are rational and protective; some are overreactions. It's important to learn how to recognize the difference.

6. You can have fear of the fear, anxiety about anxiety, worry about worry, nervousness about nervousness, panic about panic.

7. Besides emotions such as anxiety, nervousness, worry, concern, and panic, that are directly indicative of varying degrees of fear, fear is connected to emotional pain in three ways:

   1. Mislabeling emotional pain as "afraid"
   2. Fear behind the pain
   3. Fear of the pain

Part Two

Why You Feel What You Feel

"When it comes to anxiety,
thought suppression doesn't work.
Observation of thoughts does."

—Jill Stoddard

Part Two

17. Own Your Thoughts and Feelings

Owning your thoughts and feelings, and letting other people own theirs, is an important concept for dealing with emotions in a healthy way. It creates an attitude that makes it easier to take an honest look at what's going on for you, present your thoughts and feelings in a tactful way, and hear other people's perspective with less angst.

What does it mean to own thoughts and feelings?

Your thoughts and feelings create your problems, opinions, wants, and needs.

Your thoughts and feelings may be different than they were five minutes or five years ago; they may be different than they will be in the near or distant future; or they may be the same. They are just what you've got going on right now in the moment.

Your thoughts and feelings are created in this moment from 3 things:

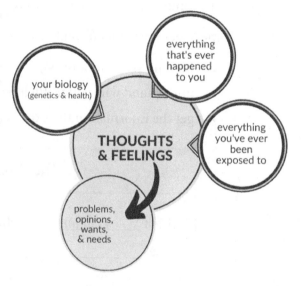

1. Your biology (including your genetics and your health)

2. Everything that's ever happened to you

3. Everything you've ever been exposed to

If you own your stuff (thoughts, feelings, problems, opinions, wants, and needs), you can express them from a position of ownership—just putting them out there for consideration. When you own your stuff, you:

- ☑ Don't expect someone else to change just because you've got a problem, want, or need

- ☑ Don't expect that others will adopt your opinion

- ☑ Can be less intimidated about voicing your ideas because you're just offering them for consideration

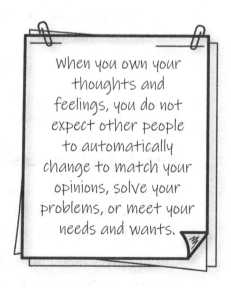

When you own your thoughts and feelings, you do not expect other people to automatically change to match your opinions, solve your problems, or meet your needs and wants.

If you let other people own their stuff, you can:

- ☑ Listen to their problems/opinions/wants/needs without feeling threatened

- ☑ Consider what they have going on

- ☑ Make your own decisions about what you think and feel about the subject

18. "I" Messages

Based on a concept that first appeared in *P.E.T., Parent Effectiveness Training* by Dr. Thomas Gordon, *"I" messages* (also known as *I-statements*) are a very effective and tactful way to talk to yourself and to others.

"I" messages are a formula for owning your stuff. They shine a light on *your* experience of things and are a great way to get the information your emotions have to offer. They help you process what you are feeling and why, and help you express your thoughts and feelings with tact (a combination of honesty and respect).

"I" messages help you efficiently:

- identify your emotion(s),
- understand why you feel/felt what you feel/felt, and
- get the information the experience has to offer.

The Basic "I" Message Formula

I feel/felt _____*emotion*_____ when _____*situation*_____

because _____*reason*_____ .

Examples of "I" messages

I felt _appreciated_ when _they thanked me for making dinner_ because _then I knew they recognized my effort._

I felt _lonely_ when _my dog died_ because _he was my companion for twelve years_.

I feel _anxious_ when _I read out loud_ because _my dyslexia makes it difficult and people might think that I'm stupid_.

Benefits for processing current and old emotions

"I" messages give you so much clarity that the burden part of the emotions is often gone after you create the message. (It's like the emotion has accomplished its job of giving you information and the release valve opens up so the rest of the emotion can move on out.)

They are very useful for understanding what's going on for you in the current moment, and they are equally valuable for processing the backlog of emotions stored in your containers. That, in turn, helps make room in your emotion containers for new stuff so that you are less likely to overreact.

"I" message tips

"I" messages help you take ownership of your emotional experience and are simultaneously honest and respectful. You may have to work at filling in the component parts of the message. Sometimes it will come to you quickly what the emotion is, what the situation is, and why you feel or felt the emotion. Other times it could take a few minutes or days.

Sometimes the *because* part of the "I" message is already covered by the *when* part, but most of the time, even if you have to push yourself a little to come up with the *because*, it is your reservoir of really useful information. It's why you feel what you feel or felt what you felt. It's the part where you're taking ownership of your thoughts and feelings.

"I" message practice. Make "I" messages for a couple of times you felt panicked, anxious, nervous, or worried.

I felt _____

when _____

_____

_____

because _____

_____

_____

_____

I felt _____

when _____

_____

_____

because _____

_____

_____

_____

19. "I" Message Variations

In using the "I" message formula for decades myself and with clients, I've noticed that the basic formula doesn't quite fit sometimes. Sometimes it works better with some minor adjustments. One set of adjustments involve replacing "when" with alternatives such as "to," "that," "of," or "about."

Reminder of the basic formula:

I feel/felt _____*emotion*_____ when _____*situation*_____

because _____*reason*_____ .

Variation examples

1. *to* instead of *when*

I <u>feel</u>/felt _____*afraid*_____ to _____*fly*_____

because _____*I had the bad experience with turbulence that one time*_____ .

2. *that* instead of *when*

I <u>feel</u>/felt _____*grateful*_____ that _____*my family lives nearby*_____

because _____*I get to see them often*_____ .

3. *of* instead of *when*

I feel/<u>felt</u> _____*jealous*_____ of _____*my older brother*_____

because _____*he got to do a lot of things my parents didn't let me do*_____ .

4. *about* instead of *when*

I <u>feel</u>/felt _____*regret*_____ about _____*making that choice*_____

because _____*it got me in trouble*_____ .

Needs Tip

Some people who teach "I" messages say to follow it up with "I need you to do x." I disagree. Don't routinely follow your "I" message with a demand. Give the listener a chance to consider what you've said. Make room for them to also have a perspective. Plus—we have few actual *needs* but may have many *wants*.

Practice making "I" messages with comfortable emotions. For each set below: choose an emotion from the list, underline the word choices (feel/felt, when/to/that/of/about) that work for your sentence, and fill in the formula blanks.

I feel/felt _____

when/to/that/of/about _____

_____

_____

because _____

_____

_____

_____

I feel/felt _____

when/to/that/of/about _____

_____

_____

because _____

_____

_____

_____

I feel/felt _____

when/to/that/of/about _____

_____

_____

because _____

_____

_____

_____

- ❏ Accepted
- ❏ Acknowledged
- ❏ Amused
- ❏ Appreciated
- ❏ Attracted
- ❏ Attractive
- ❏ Calm
- ❏ Capable
- ❏ Caring
- ❏ Competent
- ❏ Confident
- ❏ Connected
- ❏ Considered
- ❏ Content
- ❏ Creative
- ❏ Curious
- ❏ Delighted
- ❏ Empowered
- ❏ Encouraged
- ❏ Enthusiastic
- ❏ Excited
- ❏ Exhilarated
- ❏ Grateful
- ❏ Happy
- ❏ Hopeful
- ❏ Important
- ❏ Included
- ❏ Independent
- ❏ Inspired
- ❏ Interested
- ❏ Liberated
- ❏ Loved
- ❏ Nurtured
- ❏ Passionate
- ❏ Protected
- ❏ Proud
- ❏ Reassured
- ❏ Relaxed
- ❏ Relieved
- ❏ Respected
- ❏ Safe
- ❏ Satisfied
- ❏ Secure
- ❏ Stimulated
- ❏ Supported
- ❏ Surprised
- ❏ Trusted
- ❏ Trusting
- ❏ Understood
- ❏ Valued
- ❏ Welcome

- ❑ Abandoned
- ❑ Afraid
- ❑ Angry (secondary)
- ❑ Anxious
- ❑ Belittled
- ❑ Betrayed
- ❑ Concerned
- ❑ Confused
- ❑ Controlled
- ❑ Deceived
- ❑ Defeated
- ❑ Defensive
- ❑ Devastated
- ❑ Disappointed
- ❑ Disconnected
- ❑ Discounted
- ❑ Discouraged
- ❑ Disrespected
- ❑ Embarrassed
- ❑ Excluded
- ❑ Foolish
- ❑ Frustrated
- ❑ Grief
- ❑ Guilty
- ❑ Humiliated
- ❑ Inadequate
- ❑ Inferior
- ❑ Insecure
- ❑ Jealous
- ❑ Lonely
- ❑ Manipulated
- ❑ Nervous
- ❑ Obligated
- ❑ Offended
- ❑ Overwhelmed
- ❑ Panic
- ❑ Powerless
- ❑ Pressured
- ❑ Regret
- ❑ Rejected
- ❑ Resentful
- ❑ Sad
- ❑ Shame
- ❑ Shocked
- ❑ Surprised
- ❑ Trapped
- ❑ Unappreciated
- ❑ Unattractive
- ❑ Violated
- ❑ Vulnerable
- ❑ Worried

Practice making "I" messages with uncomfortable emotions. For each set below: choose an emotion from the list, underline the word choices (feel/felt, when/to/that/of/about) that work for your sentence, and fill in the formula blanks.

I feel/felt _____

when/to/that/of/about _____

_____

_____

because _____

_____

_____

_____

I feel/felt _____

when/to/that/of/about _____

_____

_____

because _____

_____

_____

_____

I feel/felt _____

when/to/that/of/about _____

_____

_____

because _____

_____

_____

_____

20. Multiple Becauses

Sometimes there's more than one *because* for a situation:

I feel _____*regret*_____ about _____*making that choice*_____

because _____*it got me in trouble*_____ ,

and because _____*it went against goals I've set for myself*_____ ,

and because _*it, unfortunately, fits an unhealthy impulsive pattern I've got going on*_ .

Multiple because practice. Think of a time that you had more than one reason you felt a particular emotion connected to a situation. Complete the "I" message with as many *becauses* as you can come up with.

I felt _____

when/to/that/of/about _____

_____

_____

because _____

_____

_____

and because _____

_____

_____

and because _____

_____

_____

and because _____

_____

_____

Sometimes the *because* part of the "I" message can be a clue that you are overreacting.

When you write or say an "I" message, you might realize that the size of the emotion doesn't seem warranted by the *because* of the "I" message or the situation in general. It doesn't seem to fit. It seems like more emotion than should be associated with what just happened.

That can lead you to figure out the cause of your overreaction. It could be a Direct Hit into that same emotion from another time, or an Add-On (many different uncomfortable or painful emotions are adding on to each other). Then you can make "I" messages for those situations and emotions.

For example, let's say this is an initial "I" message:

I felt _____*anxious*_____ when _____*he didn't call*_____

because _____*I thought something bad had happened*_____ .

After writing or saying that "I" message, you might realize that this was an overreaction.

Then you can check in with yourself whether your overreaction is a result of a Direct Hit into that container of the same emotion or an Add-On to co-occurring emotions.

Direct Hit scenario

If it's a Direct Hit into your anxiety container, your additional "I" messages could be about other times you felt anxious. They may be related to this situation or not.

Another "I" message for something similar that happened could be:

I feel _____*anxious*_____ about _____*traffic*_____

because _____*my dad was badly hurt in a car accident when I was 12*_____ .

An "I" message like this, that is related to the past, could lead to the insight that you tend to be overanxious about where someone you love is because of something anxiety-producing that happened long ago.

It can point out the source of your overreaction so that you can work on relaxing in similar situations while you also work on processing the backlog of emotions you tapped into.

ANXIETY

Other anxiety "I" messages from non-related events could be:

I felt _____anxious_____ when _____I was running late for work_____

because _____my parents were super strict about getting places on time_____.

and/or

I felt _____anxious_____ about _____my grades in school_____

because _____I had trouble with reading and focus_____.

etc.

There could be many anxious "I" messages that fit for you, and it could lead to an insight like "Wow, I've got a lot of past stuff in my anxiety container."

The good news is that once you know about overreactions, catching yourself in a Direct Hit overreaction can point you toward a container of emotional pain that needs to be processed. ("I" messages are an excellent resource for that processing.) Your efforts can pay off in reduced frequency and magnitude of overreactions, and lessen your general emotional pain load.

Add-On scenario

If you're dealing with an Add-On overreaction, the "I" messages might look like this:

The initial "I" message:

I felt _____anxious_____ when _____he didn't call_____

because _____I thought something bad had happened_____.

And another "I" message for something that happened that same day:

I felt _____embarrassed_____

when _____I was trying on clothes at the store_____

because _____I didn't fit into my usual size_____.

This can lead to the aha moment of, "Oh, I overreacted about the call because I was feeling bad about my weight!"

22. Overreaction Processing Practice

Think of a time when your panic, anxiety, nervousness, or worry was an overreaction. Describe the situation.

_____
_____
_____
_____
_____
_____
_____

Make an "I" message for the situation. Check the emotion you were feeling at the time and complete the "I" message.

I felt   ☐ panic   ☐ anxious   ☐ nervous   ☐ worried

when/to/that/of/about _____
_____
_____
_____

because _____
_____
_____

Direct Hit or Add-On? Check the box for whether your overreaction was a Direct Hit tapping into that same emotion from another time or an Add-On doubling or tripling up with other sources of emotional discomfort around the same time.

☐ Direct Hit   ☐ Add-On

Make "I" messages for what you were tapping into or adding on

to. Choose emotions from the list and complete the "I' message formulas. (If you have more to write, you can also use journal pages in Part Three.)

I felt _____

when/to/that/of/about _____

_____

_____

because _____

_____

_____

_____

_____

I felt _____

when/to/that/of/about _____

_____

_____

because _____

_____

_____

_____

_____

Reflection. Write about any insights gained from processing this overreaction.

_____

_____

_____

_____

_____

_____

_____

❑ Abandoned
❑ Afraid
❑ Angry (secondary)
❑ Anxious
❑ Belittled
❑ Betrayed
❑ Concerned
❑ Confused
❑ Controlled
❑ Deceived
❑ Defeated
❑ Defensive
❑ Devastated
❑ Disappointed
❑ Disconnected
❑ Discounted
❑ Discouraged
❑ Disrespected
❑ Embarrassed
❑ Excluded
❑ Foolish
❑ Frustrated
❑ Grief
❑ Guilty
❑ Humiliated
❑ Inadequate
❑ Inferior
❑ Insecure
❑ Jealous
❑ Lonely
❑ Manipulated
❑ Nervous
❑ Obligated
❑ Offended
❑ Overwhelmed
❑ Panic
❑ Powerless
❑ Pressured
❑ Regret
❑ Rejected
❑ Resentful
❑ Sad
❑ Shame
❑ Shocked
❑ Surprised
❑ Trapped
❑ Unappreciated
❑ Unattractive
❑ Violated
❑ Vulnerable
❑ Worried

Think of a time that you felt angry. Describe the situation.

_____

_____

_____

_____

_____

_____

Make an "I" message for the situation.

I felt angry when/to/that/of/about _____

_____

_____

_____

because _____

_____

_____

_____

What was under the anger? Check the emotion boxes on the next page for emotions that were under the anger. (There may be one or many.)

Make "I" messages for the emotions that were under your anger.

Choose emotions from the list and fill in the "I" message formula blanks. (If you have more to write, you can also use journal pages in Part Three.)

I felt _____

when/to/that/of/about _____

_____

_____

because _____

_____

_____

_____

I felt _____

when/to/that/of/about _____

_____

_____

because _____

_____

_____

_____

Reflection. Write about any insights gained from processing this anger event.

_____

_____

_____

_____

_____

_____

- ❏ Abandoned
- ❏ Afraid
- ❏ Angry (secondary)
- ❏ Anxious
- ❏ Belittled
- ❏ Betrayed
- ❏ Concerned
- ❏ Confused
- ❏ Controlled
- ❏ Deceived
- ❏ Defeated
- ❏ Defensive
- ❏ Devastated
- ❏ Disappointed
- ❏ Disconnected
- ❏ Discounted
- ❏ Discouraged
- ❏ Disrespected
- ❏ Embarrassed
- ❏ Excluded
- ❏ Foolish
- ❏ Frustrated
- ❏ Grief
- ❏ Guilty
- ❏ Humiliated
- ❏ Inadequate
- ❏ Inferior
- ❏ Insecure
- ❏ Jealous
- ❏ Lonely
- ❏ Manipulated
- ❏ Nervous
- ❏ Obligated
- ❏ Offended
- ❏ Overwhelmed
- ❏ Panic
- ❏ Powerless
- ❏ Pressured
- ❏ Regret
- ❏ Rejected
- ❏ Resentful
- ❏ Sad
- ❏ Shame
- ❏ Shocked
- ❏ Surprised
- ❏ Trapped
- ❏ Unappreciated
- ❏ Unattractive
- ❏ Violated
- ❏ Vulnerable
- ❏ Worried

45

24. Processing Stored Anxiety

Unprocessed emotional pain from past experiences doesn't just go away; it gets stored. That stored emotion can get triggered by new events and create overreactions. If you become more anxious, worried, or nervous than is warranted by current circumstances, you are probably tapping into stored emotional pain and could benefit from processing the backlog so that it can be released.

The sources of your stored emotions are unique to you. Some people have a large traumatic experience in their past that is unresolved, some have many similar experiences that piled up, some have one or a few experiences that may not seem all that big but didn't get processed at the time and got stuck.

The good news about Direct Hit overreactions is that once you know to look for them, and how to recognize them, they point to emotional containers that need attention.

Besides the emotions that made my 101 Emotions list, I find that many people who suffer from anxiety, nervousness, or worry have a full container of feeling *not-good-enough*. I didn't include it on the list since I used only single words, but it is a great descriptor for how many people feel, and it's a good one to consider when you're looking at sources of overreaction. (Some of the related single words on the 101 list may be inadequate, inferior, and foolish. Many others may also fit.)

Getting clear about the sources of stored emotion is a crucial first step toward letting it go.

Ask yourself what experiences in your past may have created panic, anxiety, nervousness, or worry.

Label the associated emotions and make "I" messages for those situations.

The emotional sting from experiences is sometimes released automatically through "I" messages. It may also be helpful to do some further processing:

- Write more about the experiences. (You may want to use the journal pages in Part Three or the Additional Reflections lined pages at the back of the workbook.)

- Visualize releasing the emotional pain and stress. (See page 173 for a releasing visualization or give my *Release and Refresh Emotional Detox Hypnosis* a try.)

- Talk to a trusted friend, family member, or counselor. (See page 177 for tips on reaching out, and Chapter 66: Anxiety Relief Therapies.)

Release & Refresh Emotional Detox Hypnosis

Hypnosis MP3 to help you let go of stored emotions
available at annsilvers.com

Release & Refresh
Hypnosis for letting go by Ann Silvers, M.A.

Anxiety-provoking experiences from the past. List some of your past experiences that may be the source of stored panic, anxiety, worry, or nervousness.

_____
_____
_____
_____
_____
_____
_____

Make an "I" message for some of the experiences. (You can use the upcoming journal pages in Part Three to write more if you like.)

I felt ☐ panic ☐ anxious ☐ nervous ☐ worried
when/to/that/of/about _____
_____
_____

because _____
_____
_____
_____

I felt ☐ panic ☐ anxious ☐ nervous ☐ worried
when/to/that/of/about _____
_____
_____

because _____
_____
_____
_____

25. Why You Feel What You Feel Summary

1. It's important to own your thoughts and feelings.

2. Your thoughts and feelings can change or stay the same. Thoughts and feelings are created by your biology, everything that's happened to you, and everything you've been exposed to.

3. "I" messages help you process what you are feeling and why, own your thoughts and feelings, and express them with tact.

4. The basic "I" message formula:

   I feel/felt _____*emotion*_____ when _____*situation*_____

   because _____*reason*_____ .

5. Sometimes, the *when* in "I" messages is better replaced with *to*, *that*, *of*, or *about*.

6. Sometimes, there's more than one *because* for an "I" message.

7. "I" messages can help you catch overreactions: when the size of your *because* doesn't fit the situation, check whether you're experiencing a Direct Hit or Add-On overreaction.

8. When you feel angry, you can make an "I" message for the anger, but it's even more important to figure out what uncomfortable emotions are under the anger and make the related "I" messages for those emotions.

9. "I" messages are one powerful way to process stored emotions.

Use the pages of Part Three to journal about times you feel or felt panicky, anxious, nervous, or worried.

Journaling Pages

"As the number of studies increased,
it became clear that writing was a far more powerful tool
for healing than anyone had ever imagined."

—James W. Pennebaker

26. Journaling for Anxiety Relief

In the 1980s, journaling research pioneer James W. Pennebaker found that people's mental and physical health improved after they wrote about stressful situations, but *only if* the writing included their emotions. Study participants who wrote about stressful events but did not include their emotional experience—did not experience the health improvements of the other group.

Subsequent studies by Pennebaker and other researchers, such as Susan Lutgendorf, support that the mere recounting of facts related to stressful events isn't as helpful as journaling that includes the connected emotions, thoughts, and insights. When all three components are present in the journaling, the writers tend to improve physically and psychologically (less illness, less stress, less depression, better grades, and other well-being markers).

My experiences from a lifetime of dealing with my own traumas and challenges, and decades helping counseling clients deal with theirs, led me to the same conclusions as these researchers.

The journaling pages in this section are organized with prompts to help you dive into, and express, all three components that make up the most helpful journaling practices:

Emotions • Thoughts • Insights

Working with these journal pages can help you:

- Figure out why you're feeling panicked, anxious, worried, or nervous in the present
- Formulate "I" messages so you can express your thoughts and feelings with tact
- Uncover sources of overreaction
- Process emotional backlog from the past
- Make plans for bettering your life

The journal pages are organized in sets of two pages. Each set of two journal pages includes:

- A list of uncomfortable emotions to help you label what you feel/felt
- Prompts for completing "I" messages
- An area for More "I" messages and/or freewriting
- An area for Insights/Learning
- A section for Next steps

The journal pages are in the middle of this workbook
so that you can begin using them even though you will be learning more about anxiety as you go through the information and exercises in Parts Four to Eight.
Use the journal pages whenever you like
and continue to move through the rest of the workbook too.

Freewriting

Besides prompts for writing "I" messages, the journal pages have space for *freewriting*. Freewriting is a form of journaling that can be very cathartic. It can lead to insights, relieve the burden of current emotion, and help you let go of stored emotion.

When you freewrite, you write everything that comes to mind whether it is on topic or not. You don't worry about punctuation, grammar, or structure because those distractions could get in the way of your process. Even the lines on the paper don't confine your expression. You are inviting the thoughts that you might otherwise censor in yourself and it can provide a window into your reality.

Freewriting could be the next step after writing "I" messages or an initial step spurred on by an emotion, event, or situation. (You may want to reverse the order of writing that is prompted in the journal pages by beginning with freewriting and then going back and making related "I" messages.)

Insights/Learning

The "I" messages and freewriting help you process the thoughts and feelings connected to challenges, and the Insights/Learning section of each set of journaling pages gives you an opportunity to harvest the wisdom from the challenges you write about.

You may have immediate insights/learning while you're writing, or you may want to return to this section later after more reflection time.

You won't necessarily come to any insights/learning from every journaling session. That's OK. This is <u>not</u> a test. The journal sections and prompts are <u>not</u> intended to add pressure to your life. You may have gained everything you need via the writing process itself.

Here are some questions that might help you harvest the wisdom from your emotions and experiences:

1. Do you notice any patterns? There could be patterns to what happens to you, what other people around you do, or how you respond.
2. How do the emotions and experiences impact your current life?
3. Is there something that you can give yourself a pat on the back for?
4. Do you see something you would like to change about yourself or your life?
5. Is there anything you can learn about what has worked or not worked for you in the situations?
6. Can you see anything positive that has come from the experiences?

Next Steps

Once you have the information from your emotions, you may want to do something with that information. Each set of journaling pages also has an area for noting possible next steps. This is where you can write about any action you want to consider or take based on the writing experience, insights, or learning.

Next steps could be specific, general, or just the beginning of an idea for a next step. Consider it a personal brainstorming space. You can hold yourself accountable to it, or you may decide later that it's not such a good idea after all.

Next steps could include:

- Doing something to further release the emotions (e.g., utilizing some of the ideas in Parts Four to Eight of this workbook)
- Experimenting with some of the skills listed in the upcoming chapters
- A change you want to make
- A plan for change (or a note to make a plan for the change)
- Something you want to write about in the future or research
- A question you want to ponder or find an answer for
- Emotionally healing and nurturing activities to counter the stuff you've been writing about (see Part Seven: Stress Resilience Lifestyle for ideas)
- Something that would encourage you

The next 2 pages show an example of a completed journal page set.

- ☐ Abandoned
- ☐ Afraid
- ☐ Angry (secondary)
- ☐ Anxious
- ☐ Belittled
- ☐ Betrayed
- ☐ Concerned
- ☐ Confused
- ☐ Controlled
- ☐ Deceived
- ☐ Defeated
- ☐ Defensive
- ☐ Devastated
- ☑ Disappointed
- ☐ Disconnected
- ☐ Discounted
- ☐ Discouraged
- ☐ Disrespected
- ☐ Embarrassed
- ☐ Excluded
- ☐ Foolish
- ☐ Frustrated
- ☐ Grief
- ☐ Guilty
- ☐ Humiliated
- ☐ Inadequate
- ☐ Inferior
- ☑ Insecure
- ☐ Jealous
- ☐ Lonely
- ☐ Manipulated
- ☐ Nervous
- ☐ Obligated
- ☐ Offended
- ☐ Overwhelmed
- ☐ Panic
- ☐ Powerless
- ☐ Pressured
- ☐ Regret
- ☐ Rejected
- ☐ Resentful
- ☐ Sad
- ☐ Shame
- ☐ Shocked
- ☐ Surprised
- ☐ Trapped
- ☐ Unappreciated
- ☐ Unattractive
- ☐ Violated
- ☐ Vulnerable
- ☐ Worried

JOURNALING EXAMPLE

I feel/felt ☐ panic ☑ anxious ☐ nervous ☐ worried

when/to/that/of/about   *my presentation next week*

because   *I might mess up.*

The connected emotions

Put a check mark on the list to the left next to any other relevant emotions.

"I" messages

Complete other related "I" messages. If you overreacted, include "I" messages for past experiences with the same emotion that you may have tapped into (Direct Hit overreaction) or other emotions felt at the same time (Add-On).

I feel/felt *insecure* when/to/that/of/about *the presentation*

because *I've had bad experiences with my anxiety getting in the way of my performance in the past.*

I feel/felt *disappointed* when/to/that/of/about *I get anxious about stuff like presentations*

because *I wish I could be more self-confident and not so scared.*

JOURNALING EXAMPLE

More "I" messages and/or freewriting

I'm tired of getting anxious about stuff like this. I guess that everyone gets a little nervous about presentations. I've seen interviews with actors who talk about getting nervous about performances even though they have lots of experience & seem self-confident – so I guess some nervousness is normal in these situations.

But I want to be able to do this sort of thing with a lot less anxiety.

Good news is: I've got a week left to practice some of the relaxation tips etc that I've been learning. My anxiety is down since I've been eating better (especially since I dropped the cola – Ann was right about that adding anxiety) & using the relaxation skills etc.

Insights/Learning

- It's OK to have some nervousness for presentations.
- I'm doing better with my anxiety than in the past.
    → that's encouraging
- I've got new skills for coping → also encouraging.

Next steps

Plan: Stop my brain when I imagine the presentation going badly. Tell myself "You've got this!" Visualize using my new relaxation skills and having the presentation go well. Stay away from caffeine – drink more water.

- ☐ Abandoned
- ☐ Afraid
- ☐ Angry (secondary)
- ☐ Anxious
- ☐ Belittled
- ☐ Betrayed
- ☐ Concerned
- ☐ Confused
- ☐ Controlled
- ☐ Deceived
- ☐ Defeated
- ☐ Defensive
- ☐ Devastated
- ☐ Disappointed
- ☐ Disconnected
- ☐ Discounted
- ☐ Discouraged
- ☐ Disrespected
- ☐ Embarrassed
- ☐ Excluded
- ☐ Foolish
- ☐ Frustrated
- ☐ Grief
- ☐ Guilty
- ☐ Humiliated
- ☐ Inadequate
- ☐ Inferior
- ☐ Insecure
- ☐ Jealous
- ☐ Lonely
- ☐ Manipulated
- ☐ Nervous
- ☐ Obligated
- ☐ Offended
- ☐ Overwhelmed
- ☐ Panic
- ☐ Powerless
- ☐ Pressured
- ☐ Regret
- ☐ Rejected
- ☐ Resentful
- ☐ Sad
- ☐ Shame
- ☐ Shocked
- ☐ Surprised
- ☐ Trapped
- ☐ Unappreciated
- ☐ Unattractive
- ☐ Violated
- ☐ Vulnerable
- ☐ Worried

Today's date: _____

I feel/felt   ☐ panic   ☐ anxious   ☐ nervous   ☐ worried

when/to/that/of/about _____

_____

_____

_____

because _____

_____

_____

The connected emotions

Put a check mark on the list to the left next to any other relevant emotions.

"I" messages

Complete other related "I" messages. If you overreacted, include "I" messages for past experiences with the same emotion that you may have tapped into (Direct Hit overreaction) or other emotions felt at the same time (Add-On).

I feel/felt _____ when/to/that/of/about _____

_____

_____

because _____

_____

_____

I feel/felt _____ when/to/that/of/about _____

_____

_____

because _____

_____

More "I" messages and/or freewriting

_____
_____
_____
_____
_____
_____
_____
_____
_____
_____
_____
_____
_____

Insights/Learning

_____
_____
_____

Next steps

_____
_____
_____
_____

- ☐ Abandoned
- ☐ Afraid
- ☐ Angry (secondary)
- ☐ Anxious
- ☐ Belittled
- ☐ Betrayed
- ☐ Concerned
- ☐ Confused
- ☐ Controlled
- ☐ Deceived
- ☐ Defeated
- ☐ Defensive
- ☐ Devastated
- ☐ Disappointed
- ☐ Disconnected
- ☐ Discounted
- ☐ Discouraged
- ☐ Disrespected
- ☐ Embarrassed
- ☐ Excluded
- ☐ Foolish
- ☐ Frustrated
- ☐ Grief
- ☐ Guilty
- ☐ Humiliated
- ☐ Inadequate
- ☐ Inferior
- ☐ Insecure
- ☐ Jealous
- ☐ Lonely
- ☐ Manipulated
- ☐ Nervous
- ☐ Obligated
- ☐ Offended
- ☐ Overwhelmed
- ☐ Panic
- ☐ Powerless
- ☐ Pressured
- ☐ Regret
- ☐ Rejected
- ☐ Resentful
- ☐ Sad
- ☐ Shame
- ☐ Shocked
- ☐ Surprised
- ☐ Trapped
- ☐ Unappreciated
- ☐ Unattractive
- ☐ Violated
- ☐ Vulnerable
- ☐ Worried

Today's date: _____

I feel/felt   ☐ panic   ☐ anxious   ☐ nervous   ☐ worried

when/to/that/of/about _____

_____

_____

_____

because _____

_____

_____

The connected emotions

Put a check mark on the list to the left next to any other relevant emotions.

"I" messages

Complete other related "I" messages. If you overreacted, include "I" messages for past experiences with the same emotion that you may have tapped into (Direct Hit overreaction) or other emotions felt at the same time (Add-On).

I feel/felt _____ when/to/that/of/about _____

_____

_____

because _____

_____

_____

I feel/felt _____ when/to/that/of/about _____

_____

_____

because _____

_____

_____

More "I" messages and/or freewriting

Insights/Learning

Next steps

- ☐ Abandoned
- ☐ Afraid
- ☐ Angry (secondary)
- ☐ Anxious
- ☐ Belittled
- ☐ Betrayed
- ☐ Concerned
- ☐ Confused
- ☐ Controlled
- ☐ Deceived
- ☐ Defeated
- ☐ Defensive
- ☐ Devastated
- ☐ Disappointed
- ☐ Disconnected
- ☐ Discounted
- ☐ Discouraged
- ☐ Disrespected
- ☐ Embarrassed
- ☐ Excluded
- ☐ Foolish
- ☐ Frustrated
- ☐ Grief
- ☐ Guilty
- ☐ Humiliated
- ☐ Inadequate
- ☐ Inferior
- ☐ Insecure
- ☐ Jealous
- ☐ Lonely
- ☐ Manipulated
- ☐ Nervous
- ☐ Obligated
- ☐ Offended
- ☐ Overwhelmed
- ☐ Panic
- ☐ Powerless
- ☐ Pressured
- ☐ Regret
- ☐ Rejected
- ☐ Resentful
- ☐ Sad
- ☐ Shame
- ☐ Shocked
- ☐ Surprised
- ☐ Trapped
- ☐ Unappreciated
- ☐ Unattractive
- ☐ Violated
- ☐ Vulnerable
- ☐ Worried

Today's date: _____

I feel/felt   ☐ panic   ☐ anxious   ☐ nervous   ☐ worried

when/to/that/of/about _____

_____

_____

_____

because _____

_____

_____

The connected emotions

Put a check mark on the list to the left next to any other relevant emotions.

"I" messages

Complete other related "I" messages. If you overreacted, include "I" messages for past experiences with the same emotion that you may have tapped into (Direct Hit overreaction) or other emotions felt at the same time (Add-On).

I feel/felt _____ when/to/that/of/about _____

_____

_____

because _____

_____

_____

I feel/felt _____ when/to/that/of/about _____

_____

_____

because _____

_____

_____

More "I" messages and/or freewriting

_____

_____

_____

_____

_____

_____

_____

_____

_____

_____

_____

_____

_____

_____

Insights/Learning

_____

_____

_____

Next steps

_____

_____

_____

_____

- ❏ Abandoned
- ❏ Afraid
- ❏ Angry (secondary)
- ❏ Anxious
- ❏ Belittled
- ❏ Betrayed
- ❏ Concerned
- ❏ Confused
- ❏ Controlled
- ❏ Deceived
- ❏ Defeated
- ❏ Defensive
- ❏ Devastated
- ❏ Disappointed
- ❏ Disconnected
- ❏ Discounted
- ❏ Discouraged
- ❏ Disrespected
- ❏ Embarrassed
- ❏ Excluded
- ❏ Foolish
- ❏ Frustrated
- ❏ Grief
- ❏ Guilty
- ❏ Humiliated
- ❏ Inadequate
- ❏ Inferior
- ❏ Insecure
- ❏ Jealous
- ❏ Lonely
- ❏ Manipulated
- ❏ Nervous
- ❏ Obligated
- ❏ Offended
- ❏ Overwhelmed
- ❏ Panic
- ❏ Powerless
- ❏ Pressured
- ❏ Regret
- ❏ Rejected
- ❏ Resentful
- ❏ Sad
- ❏ Shame
- ❏ Shocked
- ❏ Surprised
- ❏ Trapped
- ❏ Unappreciated
- ❏ Unattractive
- ❏ Violated
- ❏ Vulnerable
- ❏ Worried

Today's date: _____

I feel/felt ❏ panic ❏ anxious ❏ nervous ❏ worried

when/to/that/of/about _____

_____

_____

_____

because _____

_____

_____

The connected emotions

Put a check mark on the list to the left next to any other relevant emotions.

"I" messages

Complete other related "I" messages. If you overreacted, include "I" messages for past experiences with the same emotion that you may have tapped into (Direct Hit overreaction) or other emotions felt at the same time (Add-On).

I feel/felt _____ when/to/that/of/about _____

_____

because _____

_____

_____

I feel/felt _____ when/to/that/of/about _____

_____

because _____

_____

_____

More "I" messages and/or freewriting

_____
_____
_____
_____
_____
_____
_____
_____
_____
_____
_____
_____
_____
_____

Insights/Learning

_____
_____
_____

Next steps

_____
_____
_____
_____

- ❏ Abandoned
- ❏ Afraid
- ❏ Angry (secondary)
- ❏ Anxious
- ❏ Belittled
- ❏ Betrayed
- ❏ Concerned
- ❏ Confused
- ❏ Controlled
- ❏ Deceived
- ❏ Defeated
- ❏ Defensive
- ❏ Devastated
- ❏ Disappointed
- ❏ Disconnected
- ❏ Discounted
- ❏ Discouraged
- ❏ Disrespected
- ❏ Embarrassed
- ❏ Excluded
- ❏ Foolish
- ❏ Frustrated
- ❏ Grief
- ❏ Guilty
- ❏ Humiliated
- ❏ Inadequate
- ❏ Inferior
- ❏ Insecure
- ❏ Jealous
- ❏ Lonely
- ❏ Manipulated
- ❏ Nervous
- ❏ Obligated
- ❏ Offended
- ❏ Overwhelmed
- ❏ Panic
- ❏ Powerless
- ❏ Pressured
- ❏ Regret
- ❏ Rejected
- ❏ Resentful
- ❏ Sad
- ❏ Shame
- ❏ Shocked
- ❏ Surprised
- ❏ Trapped
- ❏ Unappreciated
- ❏ Unattractive
- ❏ Violated
- ❏ Vulnerable
- ❏ Worried

Today's date: _____

I feel/felt   ❏ panic   ❏ anxious   ❏ nervous   ❏ worried

when/to/that/of/about _____

_____

_____

_____

because _____

_____

_____

The connected emotions

Put a check mark on the list to the left next to any other relevant emotions.

"I" messages

Complete other related "I" messages. If you overreacted, include "I" messages for past experiences with the same emotion that you may have tapped into (Direct Hit overreaction) or other emotions felt at the same time (Add-On).

I feel/felt _____ when/to/that/of/about _____

_____

_____

because _____

_____

_____

I feel/felt _____ when/to/that/of/about _____

_____

_____

because _____

_____

_____

More "I" messages and/or freewriting

_____
_____
_____
_____
_____
_____
_____
_____
_____
_____
_____
_____
_____
_____

Insights/Learning

_____
_____
_____

Next steps

_____
_____
_____
_____

- ☐ Abandoned
- ☐ Afraid
- ☐ Angry (secondary)
- ☐ Anxious
- ☐ Belittled
- ☐ Betrayed
- ☐ Concerned
- ☐ Confused
- ☐ Controlled
- ☐ Deceived
- ☐ Defeated
- ☐ Defensive
- ☐ Devastated
- ☐ Disappointed
- ☐ Disconnected
- ☐ Discounted
- ☐ Discouraged
- ☐ Disrespected
- ☐ Embarrassed
- ☐ Excluded
- ☐ Foolish
- ☐ Frustrated
- ☐ Grief
- ☐ Guilty
- ☐ Humiliated
- ☐ Inadequate
- ☐ Inferior
- ☐ Insecure
- ☐ Jealous
- ☐ Lonely
- ☐ Manipulated
- ☐ Nervous
- ☐ Obligated
- ☐ Offended
- ☐ Overwhelmed
- ☐ Panic
- ☐ Powerless
- ☐ Pressured
- ☐ Regret
- ☐ Rejected
- ☐ Resentful
- ☐ Sad
- ☐ Shame
- ☐ Shocked
- ☐ Surprised
- ☐ Trapped
- ☐ Unappreciated
- ☐ Unattractive
- ☐ Violated
- ☐ Vulnerable
- ☐ Worried

Today's date: _____

I feel/felt   ☐ panic   ☐ anxious   ☐ nervous   ☐ worried

when/to/that/of/about _____
_____
_____
_____

because _____
_____
_____

The connected emotions

Put a check mark on the list to the left next to any other relevant emotions.

"I" messages

Complete other related "I" messages. If you overreacted, include "I" messages for past experiences with the same emotion that you may have tapped into (Direct Hit overreaction) or other emotions felt at the same time (Add-On).

I feel/felt _____ when/to/that/of/about _____
_____
_____

because _____
_____
_____
_____

I feel/felt _____ when/to/that/of/about _____
_____
_____

because _____
_____
_____

More "I" messages and/or freewriting

Insights/Learning

Next steps

- ☐ Abandoned
- ☐ Afraid
- ☐ Angry (secondary)
- ☐ Anxious
- ☐ Belittled
- ☐ Betrayed
- ☐ Concerned
- ☐ Confused
- ☐ Controlled
- ☐ Deceived
- ☐ Defeated
- ☐ Defensive
- ☐ Devastated
- ☐ Disappointed
- ☐ Disconnected
- ☐ Discounted
- ☐ Discouraged
- ☐ Disrespected
- ☐ Embarrassed
- ☐ Excluded
- ☐ Foolish
- ☐ Frustrated
- ☐ Grief
- ☐ Guilty
- ☐ Humiliated
- ☐ Inadequate
- ☐ Inferior
- ☐ Insecure
- ☐ Jealous
- ☐ Lonely
- ☐ Manipulated
- ☐ Nervous
- ☐ Obligated
- ☐ Offended
- ☐ Overwhelmed
- ☐ Panic
- ☐ Powerless
- ☐ Pressured
- ☐ Regret
- ☐ Rejected
- ☐ Resentful
- ☐ Sad
- ☐ Shame
- ☐ Shocked
- ☐ Surprised
- ☐ Trapped
- ☐ Unappreciated
- ☐ Unattractive
- ☐ Violated
- ☐ Vulnerable
- ☐ Worried

Today's date: _____

I feel/felt   ☐ panic   ☐ anxious   ☐ nervous   ☐ worried

when/to/that/of/about _____

_____

_____

_____

because _____

_____

_____

The connected emotions

Put a check mark on the list to the left next to any other relevant emotions.

"I" messages

Complete other related "I" messages. If you overreacted, include "I" messages for past experiences with the same emotion that you may have tapped into (Direct Hit overreaction) or other emotions felt at the same time (Add-On).

I feel/felt _____ when/to/that/of/about _____

_____

_____

because _____

_____

_____

I feel/felt _____ when/to/that/of/about _____

_____

_____

because _____

_____

More "I" messages and/or freewriting

_____

_____

_____

_____

_____

_____

_____

_____

_____

_____

_____

_____

_____

Insights/Learning

_____

_____

_____

Next steps

_____

_____

_____

_____

- ❏ Abandoned
- ❏ Afraid
- ❏ Angry (secondary)
- ❏ Anxious
- ❏ Belittled
- ❏ Betrayed
- ❏ Concerned
- ❏ Confused
- ❏ Controlled
- ❏ Deceived
- ❏ Defeated
- ❏ Defensive
- ❏ Devastated
- ❏ Disappointed
- ❏ Disconnected
- ❏ Discounted
- ❏ Discouraged
- ❏ Disrespected
- ❏ Embarrassed
- ❏ Excluded
- ❏ Foolish
- ❏ Frustrated
- ❏ Grief
- ❏ Guilty
- ❏ Humiliated
- ❏ Inadequate
- ❏ Inferior
- ❏ Insecure
- ❏ Jealous
- ❏ Lonely
- ❏ Manipulated
- ❏ Nervous
- ❏ Obligated
- ❏ Offended
- ❏ Overwhelmed
- ❏ Panic
- ❏ Powerless
- ❏ Pressured
- ❏ Regret
- ❏ Rejected
- ❏ Resentful
- ❏ Sad
- ❏ Shame
- ❏ Shocked
- ❏ Surprised
- ❏ Trapped
- ❏ Unappreciated
- ❏ Unattractive
- ❏ Violated
- ❏ Vulnerable
- ❏ Worried

Today's date: _____

I feel/felt ❏ panic ❏ anxious ❏ nervous ❏ worried

when/to/that/of/about _____

_____

_____

_____

because _____

_____

_____

The connected emotions

Put a check mark on the list to the left next to any other relevant emotions.

"I" messages

Complete other related "I" messages. If you overreacted, include "I" messages for past experiences with the same emotion that you may have tapped into (Direct Hit overreaction) or other emotions felt at the same time (Add-On).

I feel/felt _____ when/to/that/of/about _____

_____

_____

because _____

_____

_____

I feel/felt _____ when/to/that/of/about _____

_____

_____

because _____

_____

More "I" messages and/or freewriting

Insights/Learning

Next steps

- ☐ Abandoned
- ☐ Afraid
- ☐ Angry (secondary)
- ☐ Anxious
- ☐ Belittled
- ☐ Betrayed
- ☐ Concerned
- ☐ Confused
- ☐ Controlled
- ☐ Deceived
- ☐ Defeated
- ☐ Defensive
- ☐ Devastated
- ☐ Disappointed
- ☐ Disconnected
- ☐ Discounted
- ☐ Discouraged
- ☐ Disrespected
- ☐ Embarrassed
- ☐ Excluded
- ☐ Foolish
- ☐ Frustrated
- ☐ Grief
- ☐ Guilty
- ☐ Humiliated
- ☐ Inadequate
- ☐ Inferior
- ☐ Insecure
- ☐ Jealous
- ☐ Lonely
- ☐ Manipulated
- ☐ Nervous
- ☐ Obligated
- ☐ Offended
- ☐ Overwhelmed
- ☐ Panic
- ☐ Powerless
- ☐ Pressured
- ☐ Regret
- ☐ Rejected
- ☐ Resentful
- ☐ Sad
- ☐ Shame
- ☐ Shocked
- ☐ Surprised
- ☐ Trapped
- ☐ Unappreciated
- ☐ Unattractive
- ☐ Violated
- ☐ Vulnerable
- ☐ Worried

Today's date: _____

I feel/felt ☐ panic ☐ anxious ☐ nervous ☐ worried

when/to/that/of/about _____

_____

_____

_____

because _____

_____

_____

The connected emotions

Put a check mark on the list to the left next to any other relevant emotions.

"I" messages

Complete other related "I" messages. If you overreacted, include "I" messages for past experiences with the same emotion that you may have tapped into (Direct Hit overreaction) or other emotions felt at the same time (Add-On).

I feel/felt _____ when/to/that/of/about _____

_____

_____

because _____

_____

_____

I feel/felt _____ when/to/that/of/about _____

_____

_____

because _____

_____

More "I" messages and/or freewriting

_____
_____
_____
_____
_____
_____
_____
_____
_____
_____
_____
_____
_____
_____

Insights/Learning

_____
_____
_____

Next steps

_____
_____
_____
_____

- ❑ Abandoned
- ❑ Afraid
- ❑ Angry (secondary)
- ❑ Anxious
- ❑ Belittled
- ❑ Betrayed
- ❑ Concerned
- ❑ Confused
- ❑ Controlled
- ❑ Deceived
- ❑ Defeated
- ❑ Defensive
- ❑ Devastated
- ❑ Disappointed
- ❑ Disconnected
- ❑ Discounted
- ❑ Discouraged
- ❑ Disrespected
- ❑ Embarrassed
- ❑ Excluded
- ❑ Foolish
- ❑ Frustrated
- ❑ Grief
- ❑ Guilty
- ❑ Humiliated
- ❑ Inadequate
- ❑ Inferior
- ❑ Insecure
- ❑ Jealous
- ❑ Lonely
- ❑ Manipulated
- ❑ Nervous
- ❑ Obligated
- ❑ Offended
- ❑ Overwhelmed
- ❑ Panic
- ❑ Powerless
- ❑ Pressured
- ❑ Regret
- ❑ Rejected
- ❑ Resentful
- ❑ Sad
- ❑ Shame
- ❑ Shocked
- ❑ Surprised
- ❑ Trapped
- ❑ Unappreciated
- ❑ Unattractive
- ❑ Violated
- ❑ Vulnerable
- ❑ Worried

Today's date: _____

I feel/felt ❑ panic ❑ anxious ❑ nervous ❑ worried

when/to/that/of/about _____

_____

_____

_____

because _____

_____

_____

_____

The connected emotions

Put a check mark on the list to the left next to any other relevant emotions.

"I" messages

Complete other related "I" messages. If you overreacted, include "I" messages for past experiences with the same emotion that you may have tapped into (Direct Hit overreaction) or other emotions felt at the same time (Add-On).

I feel/felt _____ when/to/that/of/about _____

_____

_____

because _____

_____

_____

_____

I feel/felt _____ when/to/that/of/about _____

_____

_____

because _____

_____

_____

More "I" messages and/or freewriting

_____

_____

_____

_____

_____

_____

_____

_____

_____

_____

_____

_____

Insights/Learning

_____

_____

_____

Next steps

_____

_____

_____

_____

- ☐ Abandoned
- ☐ Afraid
- ☐ Angry (secondary)
- ☐ Anxious
- ☐ Belittled
- ☐ Betrayed
- ☐ Concerned
- ☐ Confused
- ☐ Controlled
- ☐ Deceived
- ☐ Defeated
- ☐ Defensive
- ☐ Devastated
- ☐ Disappointed
- ☐ Disconnected
- ☐ Discounted
- ☐ Discouraged
- ☐ Disrespected
- ☐ Embarrassed
- ☐ Excluded
- ☐ Foolish
- ☐ Frustrated
- ☐ Grief
- ☐ Guilty
- ☐ Humiliated
- ☐ Inadequate
- ☐ Inferior
- ☐ Insecure
- ☐ Jealous
- ☐ Lonely
- ☐ Manipulated
- ☐ Nervous
- ☐ Obligated
- ☐ Offended
- ☐ Overwhelmed
- ☐ Panic
- ☐ Powerless
- ☐ Pressured
- ☐ Regret
- ☐ Rejected
- ☐ Resentful
- ☐ Sad
- ☐ Shame
- ☐ Shocked
- ☐ Surprised
- ☐ Trapped
- ☐ Unappreciated
- ☐ Unattractive
- ☐ Violated
- ☐ Vulnerable
- ☐ Worried

Today's date: _____

I feel/felt ☐ panic ☐ anxious ☐ nervous ☐ worried

when/to/that/of/about _____

_____

_____

_____

because _____

_____

_____

The connected emotions

Put a check mark on the list to the left next to any other relevant emotions.

"I" messages

Complete other related "I" messages. If you overreacted, include "I" messages for past experiences with the same emotion that you may have tapped into (Direct Hit overreaction) or other emotions felt at the same time (Add-On).

I feel/felt _____ when/to/that/of/about _____

_____

_____

because _____

_____

_____

_____

I feel/felt _____ when/to/that/of/about _____

_____

_____

because _____

_____

_____

More "I" messages and/or freewriting

_____

_____

_____

_____

_____

_____

_____

_____

_____

_____

_____

_____

_____

Insights/Learning

_____

_____

_____

Next steps

_____

_____

_____

_____

- ☐ Abandoned
- ☐ Afraid
- ☐ Angry (secondary)
- ☐ Anxious
- ☐ Belittled
- ☐ Betrayed
- ☐ Concerned
- ☐ Confused
- ☐ Controlled
- ☐ Deceived
- ☐ Defeated
- ☐ Defensive
- ☐ Devastated
- ☐ Disappointed
- ☐ Disconnected
- ☐ Discounted
- ☐ Discouraged
- ☐ Disrespected
- ☐ Embarrassed
- ☐ Excluded
- ☐ Foolish
- ☐ Frustrated
- ☐ Grief
- ☐ Guilty
- ☐ Humiliated
- ☐ Inadequate
- ☐ Inferior
- ☐ Insecure
- ☐ Jealous
- ☐ Lonely
- ☐ Manipulated
- ☐ Nervous
- ☐ Obligated
- ☐ Offended
- ☐ Overwhelmed
- ☐ Panic
- ☐ Powerless
- ☐ Pressured
- ☐ Regret
- ☐ Rejected
- ☐ Resentful
- ☐ Sad
- ☐ Shame
- ☐ Shocked
- ☐ Surprised
- ☐ Trapped
- ☐ Unappreciated
- ☐ Unattractive
- ☐ Violated
- ☐ Vulnerable
- ☐ Worried

Today's date: _____

I feel/felt ☐ panic ☐ anxious ☐ nervous ☐ worried

when/to/that/of/about _____

_____

_____

_____

because _____

_____

_____

The connected emotions

Put a check mark on the list to the left next to any other relevant emotions.

"I" messages

Complete other related "I" messages. If you overreacted, include "I" messages for past experiences with the same emotion that you may have tapped into (Direct Hit overreaction) or other emotions felt at the same time (Add-On).

I feel/felt _____ when/to/that/of/about _____

_____

_____

because _____

_____

_____

I feel/felt _____ when/to/that/of/about _____

_____

_____

because _____

_____

_____

More "I" messages and/or freewriting

_____

_____

_____

_____

_____

_____

_____

_____

_____

_____

_____

_____

_____

_____

_____

Insights/Learning

_____

_____

_____

Next steps

_____

_____

_____

_____

- ☐ Abandoned
- ☐ Afraid
- ☐ Angry (secondary)
- ☐ Anxious
- ☐ Belittled
- ☐ Betrayed
- ☐ Concerned
- ☐ Confused
- ☐ Controlled
- ☐ Deceived
- ☐ Defeated
- ☐ Defensive
- ☐ Devastated
- ☐ Disappointed
- ☐ Disconnected
- ☐ Discounted
- ☐ Discouraged
- ☐ Disrespected
- ☐ Embarrassed
- ☐ Excluded
- ☐ Foolish
- ☐ Frustrated
- ☐ Grief
- ☐ Guilty
- ☐ Humiliated
- ☐ Inadequate
- ☐ Inferior
- ☐ Insecure
- ☐ Jealous
- ☐ Lonely
- ☐ Manipulated
- ☐ Nervous
- ☐ Obligated
- ☐ Offended
- ☐ Overwhelmed
- ☐ Panic
- ☐ Powerless
- ☐ Pressured
- ☐ Regret
- ☐ Rejected
- ☐ Resentful
- ☐ Sad
- ☐ Shame
- ☐ Shocked
- ☐ Surprised
- ☐ Trapped
- ☐ Unappreciated
- ☐ Unattractive
- ☐ Violated
- ☐ Vulnerable
- ☐ Worried

Today's date: _____

I feel/felt ☐ panic ☐ anxious ☐ nervous ☐ worried

when/to/that/of/about _____

_____

_____

_____

because _____

_____

_____

_____

The connected emotions

Put a check mark on the list to the left next to any other relevant emotions.

"I" messages

Complete other related "I" messages. If you overreacted, include "I" messages for past experiences with the same emotion that you may have tapped into (Direct Hit overreaction) or other emotions felt at the same time (Add-On).

I feel/felt _____ when/to/that/of/about _____

_____

_____

because _____

_____

_____

I feel/felt _____ when/to/that/of/about _____

_____

_____

because _____

_____

_____

More "I" messages and/or freewriting

Insights/Learning

Next steps

- ❏ Abandoned
- ❏ Afraid
- ❏ Angry (secondary)
- ❏ Anxious
- ❏ Belittled
- ❏ Betrayed
- ❏ Concerned
- ❏ Confused
- ❏ Controlled
- ❏ Deceived
- ❏ Defeated
- ❏ Defensive
- ❏ Devastated
- ❏ Disappointed
- ❏ Disconnected
- ❏ Discounted
- ❏ Discouraged
- ❏ Disrespected
- ❏ Embarrassed
- ❏ Excluded
- ❏ Foolish
- ❏ Frustrated
- ❏ Grief
- ❏ Guilty
- ❏ Humiliated
- ❏ Inadequate
- ❏ Inferior
- ❏ Insecure
- ❏ Jealous
- ❏ Lonely
- ❏ Manipulated
- ❏ Nervous
- ❏ Obligated
- ❏ Offended
- ❏ Overwhelmed
- ❏ Panic
- ❏ Powerless
- ❏ Pressured
- ❏ Regret
- ❏ Rejected
- ❏ Resentful
- ❏ Sad
- ❏ Shame
- ❏ Shocked
- ❏ Surprised
- ❏ Trapped
- ❏ Unappreciated
- ❏ Unattractive
- ❏ Violated
- ❏ Vulnerable
- ❏ Worried

Today's date: _____

I feel/felt ❏ panic ❏ anxious ❏ nervous ❏ worried

when/to/that/of/about _____

_____

_____

_____

because _____

_____

_____

The connected emotions

Put a check mark on the list to the left next to any other relevant emotions.

"I" messages

Complete other related "I" messages. If you overreacted, include "I" messages for past experiences with the same emotion that you may have tapped into (Direct Hit overreaction) or other emotions felt at the same time (Add-On).

I feel/felt _____ when/to/that/of/about _____

_____

_____

because _____

_____

_____

I feel/felt _____ when/to/that/of/about _____

_____

_____

because _____

_____

_____

More "I" messages and/or freewriting

_____
_____
_____
_____
_____
_____
_____
_____
_____
_____
_____
_____
_____
_____

Insights/Learning

_____
_____
_____

Next steps

_____
_____
_____
_____

- ☐ Abandoned
- ☐ Afraid
- ☐ Angry (secondary)
- ☐ Anxious
- ☐ Belittled
- ☐ Betrayed
- ☐ Concerned
- ☐ Confused
- ☐ Controlled
- ☐ Deceived
- ☐ Defeated
- ☐ Defensive
- ☐ Devastated
- ☐ Disappointed
- ☐ Disconnected
- ☐ Discounted
- ☐ Discouraged
- ☐ Disrespected
- ☐ Embarrassed
- ☐ Excluded
- ☐ Foolish
- ☐ Frustrated
- ☐ Grief
- ☐ Guilty
- ☐ Humiliated
- ☐ Inadequate
- ☐ Inferior
- ☐ Insecure
- ☐ Jealous
- ☐ Lonely
- ☐ Manipulated
- ☐ Nervous
- ☐ Obligated
- ☐ Offended
- ☐ Overwhelmed
- ☐ Panic
- ☐ Powerless
- ☐ Pressured
- ☐ Regret
- ☐ Rejected
- ☐ Resentful
- ☐ Sad
- ☐ Shame
- ☐ Shocked
- ☐ Surprised
- ☐ Trapped
- ☐ Unappreciated
- ☐ Unattractive
- ☐ Violated
- ☐ Vulnerable
- ☐ Worried

Today's date: _____

I feel/felt ☐ panic ☐ anxious ☐ nervous ☐ worried

when/to/that/of/about _____

_____

_____

because _____

_____

_____

The connected emotions

Put a check mark on the list to the left next to any other relevant emotions.

"I" messages

Complete other related "I" messages. If you overreacted, include "I" messages for past experiences with the same emotion that you may have tapped into (Direct Hit overreaction) or other emotions felt at the same time (Add-On).

I feel/felt _____ when/to/that/of/about _____

_____

_____

because _____

_____

_____

_____

I feel/felt _____ when/to/that/of/about _____

_____

_____

_____

because _____

_____

_____

More "I" messages and/or freewriting

_____
_____
_____
_____
_____
_____
_____
_____
_____
_____
_____
_____
_____
_____
_____
_____

Insights/Learning

_____
_____
_____

Next steps

_____
_____
_____
_____

- ☐ Abandoned
- ☐ Afraid
- ☐ Angry (secondary)
- ☐ Anxious
- ☐ Belittled
- ☐ Betrayed
- ☐ Concerned
- ☐ Confused
- ☐ Controlled
- ☐ Deceived
- ☐ Defeated
- ☐ Defensive
- ☐ Devastated
- ☐ Disappointed
- ☐ Disconnected
- ☐ Discounted
- ☐ Discouraged
- ☐ Disrespected
- ☐ Embarrassed
- ☐ Excluded
- ☐ Foolish
- ☐ Frustrated
- ☐ Grief
- ☐ Guilty
- ☐ Humiliated
- ☐ Inadequate
- ☐ Inferior
- ☐ Insecure
- ☐ Jealous
- ☐ Lonely
- ☐ Manipulated
- ☐ Nervous
- ☐ Obligated
- ☐ Offended
- ☐ Overwhelmed
- ☐ Panic
- ☐ Powerless
- ☐ Pressured
- ☐ Regret
- ☐ Rejected
- ☐ Resentful
- ☐ Sad
- ☐ Shame
- ☐ Shocked
- ☐ Surprised
- ☐ Trapped
- ☐ Unappreciated
- ☐ Unattractive
- ☐ Violated
- ☐ Vulnerable
- ☐ Worried

Today's date: _____

I feel/felt   ☐ panic   ☐ anxious   ☐ nervous   ☐ worried

when/to/that/of/about _____

_____

_____

_____

because _____

_____

_____

The connected emotions

Put a check mark on the list to the left next to any other relevant emotions.

"I" messages

Complete other related "I" messages. If you overreacted, include "I" messages for past experiences with the same emotion that you may have tapped into (Direct Hit overreaction) or other emotions felt at the same time (Add-On).

I feel/felt _____ when/to/that/of/about _____

_____

_____

because _____

_____

_____

I feel/felt _____ when/to/that/of/about _____

_____

_____

because _____

_____

_____

More "I" messages and/or freewriting

Insights/Learning

Next steps

- ☐ Abandoned
- ☐ Afraid
- ☐ Angry (secondary)
- ☐ Anxious
- ☐ Belittled
- ☐ Betrayed
- ☐ Concerned
- ☐ Confused
- ☐ Controlled
- ☐ Deceived
- ☐ Defeated
- ☐ Defensive
- ☐ Devastated
- ☐ Disappointed
- ☐ Disconnected
- ☐ Discounted
- ☐ Discouraged
- ☐ Disrespected
- ☐ Embarrassed
- ☐ Excluded
- ☐ Foolish
- ☐ Frustrated
- ☐ Grief
- ☐ Guilty
- ☐ Humiliated
- ☐ Inadequate
- ☐ Inferior
- ☐ Insecure
- ☐ Jealous
- ☐ Lonely
- ☐ Manipulated
- ☐ Nervous
- ☐ Obligated
- ☐ Offended
- ☐ Overwhelmed
- ☐ Panic
- ☐ Powerless
- ☐ Pressured
- ☐ Regret
- ☐ Rejected
- ☐ Resentful
- ☐ Sad
- ☐ Shame
- ☐ Shocked
- ☐ Surprised
- ☐ Trapped
- ☐ Unappreciated
- ☐ Unattractive
- ☐ Violated
- ☐ Vulnerable
- ☐ Worried

Today's date: _____

I feel/felt ☐ panic ☐ anxious ☐ nervous ☐ worried

when/to/that/of/about _____

_____

_____

_____

because _____

_____

_____

The connected emotions

Put a check mark on the list to the left next to any other relevant emotions.

"I" messages

Complete other related "I" messages. If you overreacted, include "I" messages for past experiences with the same emotion that you may have tapped into (Direct Hit overreaction) or other emotions felt at the same time (Add-On).

I feel/felt _____ when/to/that/of/about _____

_____

_____

because _____

_____

_____

I feel/felt _____ when/to/that/of/about _____

_____

_____

because _____

_____

_____

More "I" messages and/or freewriting

_____
_____
_____
_____
_____
_____
_____
_____
_____
_____
_____
_____
_____
_____

Insights/Learning

_____
_____
_____

Next steps

_____
_____
_____
_____

- ❏ Abandoned
- ❏ Afraid
- ❏ Angry (secondary)
- ❏ Anxious
- ❏ Belittled
- ❏ Betrayed
- ❏ Concerned
- ❏ Confused
- ❏ Controlled
- ❏ Deceived
- ❏ Defeated
- ❏ Defensive
- ❏ Devastated
- ❏ Disappointed
- ❏ Disconnected
- ❏ Discounted
- ❏ Discouraged
- ❏ Disrespected
- ❏ Embarrassed
- ❏ Excluded
- ❏ Foolish
- ❏ Frustrated
- ❏ Grief
- ❏ Guilty
- ❏ Humiliated
- ❏ Inadequate
- ❏ Inferior
- ❏ Insecure
- ❏ Jealous
- ❏ Lonely
- ❏ Manipulated
- ❏ Nervous
- ❏ Obligated
- ❏ Offended
- ❏ Overwhelmed
- ❏ Panic
- ❏ Powerless
- ❏ Pressured
- ❏ Regret
- ❏ Rejected
- ❏ Resentful
- ❏ Sad
- ❏ Shame
- ❏ Shocked
- ❏ Surprised
- ❏ Trapped
- ❏ Unappreciated
- ❏ Unattractive
- ❏ Violated
- ❏ Vulnerable
- ❏ Worried

Today's date: _____

I feel/felt   ❏ panic   ❏ anxious   ❏ nervous   ❏ worried

when/to/that/of/about _____

_____

_____

_____

because _____

_____

_____

The connected emotions

Put a check mark on the list to the left next to any other relevant emotions.

"I" messages

Complete other related "I" messages. If you overreacted, include "I" messages for past experiences with the same emotion that you may have tapped into (Direct Hit overreaction) or other emotions felt at the same time (Add-On).

I feel/felt _____ when/to/that/of/about _____

_____

_____

because _____

_____

_____

_____

I feel/felt _____ when/to/that/of/about _____

_____

_____

because _____

_____

_____

_____

More "I" messages and/or freewriting

_____
_____
_____
_____
_____
_____
_____
_____
_____
_____
_____
_____
_____
_____

Insights/Learning

_____
_____
_____

Next steps

_____
_____
_____
_____

Part Four

How to Relax & Reset

"Almost everything will work again
if you unplug it for a few minutes, including you."

—Anne Lamott

Part Four

Relaxation is central to dealing with anxiety. It's the opposite of what you feel when you're anxious, and it's what you crave. You want to be able to relax away the tension in your mind and your body, but it isn't as simple as wishing and making it so.

Here's a reminder of the fear hierarchy we talked about earlier:

 decreasing intensity

PANIC (immobilizing)
ANXIETY (consuming)
NERVOUSNESS / WORRY (distracting)
CONCERN *the sweet spot
_____

OBLIVIOUS / NUMB (avoiding)

When you feel stressed, panicky, anxious, nervous, or worried, it's helpful to relax your body and mind to a place of clear-headed concern. From this reset place, you can logically think about the source of the fear.

When you are relaxed, you can ask yourself:

- "What is it that I'm afraid of?"
- "Am I overreacting?"
- "What are my options for dealing with this situation?"

Then you can:

- choose an option,
- make a plan, and
- put your plan into action.

That all requires logic, and it's difficult to be logical when you're wound up by stress.

The following two chapters describe 5 relaxation techniques and 5 grounding techniques that utilize your body to reset your mind.

I offer multiple options for relaxing and resetting because different techniques work for different people, and individuals may find some of the options more or less useful depending on the circumstances. Experiment to find out which relaxation and resetting methods work for you, and in which situations.

28. Five Relaxation Techniques

Here are the five relaxation techniques that I teach my clients (and reinforce in my *Discover Calm, Anti-Anxiety Hypnosis* recording, which is available at annsilvers.com as an mp3 download). You can use any of these techniques in combination with each other, all of them, or just one—whatever works for you.

1. Take a couple of slow, deep breaths.
2. Think of a word or phrase that helps you relax or feel empowered.
3. Think of a "happy place."
4. Think about, or bring with you, an item that helps you feel relaxed or empowered.
5. Put your thumb and finger together.

1. Take a couple of slow, deep breaths.

Deep breaths are great for helping you relax physically and mentally.

These breaths help relieve stress by oxygenating your cells (including your brain and nerve endings), distracting your mind away from anxious thoughts, and massaging the vagus nerve. Your vagus nerve runs from your gut to your brain. It's involved in the regulation of many body processes, including blood pressure and heart rate. Deep breaths help massage the vagus nerve. That results in lowering your blood pressure and heart rate.

While taking a couple of deep breaths when you begin to feel anxious, nervous, or worried can help you relax, you can also increase their effectiveness by imagining that with each breath in, you are breathing in relaxation, and with each breath out, you are breathing out tension.

Breathing Tips: 1) You may have to exhale first before you can take a deep breath in.
2) How to know when you've taken a deep breath: your abdomen rises as you breathe in.

2. Think of a word or phrase that helps you relax or feel empowered.

Thinking of a word or phrase that is relaxing or calming, or that helps you feel more self-confident and empowered, may help you deal with stressful situations.

Here are some examples:

- "I'm OK." "I'll be OK." "It will be OK."
- "I'm good at this." "I can do this."
- "This too shall pass."
- "It is what it is."

You may have some other special word or phrase that helps you relax or feel empowered. Experiment with whatever might work for you.

> **What words or phrases might help?** List some words or phrases that might help you feel relaxed, calm, self-confident, or empowered when you're stressed.

3. Think of a "happy place."

A "happy place" is a vivid thought that helps you feel relaxed and/or empowered. It is great for countering the negative, stressful, anxious thoughts that typically go round and round, growing into more awful worse-than-worst-case scenarios.

A "happy place" doesn't have to be a "place" and it doesn't have to be something you have experienced in real life.

My happy place is not at all what you likely think of as a traditional happy place. My happy place is a scene from the Mel Brooks screwball comedy *Spaceballs*. It is perfect for me because the scene is perfectly matched comic relief for a situation that stimulated the only full-blown panic attacks I have experienced.

That high-anxiety event led me to get help from one of my hypnotherapist friends. When she asked me to come up with a happy place, the movie scene popped into my head.

I was too embarrassed to tell her what it was because it seemed too silly, but the thought of the scene persisted, and I have successfully used it many times to break through stress, put a smile on my face, and automatically make me feel relaxed.

A happy place can be:

- a place you have been that was relaxing, enjoyable, or empowering,
- a scene from a movie,
- a happy memory,
- a song, or
- an imaginary situation or place.

What you're going for is something that counters the stress you're feeling. It might be calming and relaxing, or it may be something that helps you feel more self-confident and empowered.

What might work as your happy place? List some ideas of potential happy places that might help you feel relaxed, calm, self-confident, and empowered when you're stressed.

Describe your happy place. Pick one of your happy place ideas to fully describe so you can vividly imagine it when you need it.

Describe what your happy place looks like.

Describe the sounds of your happy place.

Describe the smells of your happy place.

Describe what it feels like physically.

_____

_____

_____

_____

_____

Describe what it feels like emotionally.

_____

_____

_____

_____

_____

4. Think about, or bring with you, an item that helps you feel relaxed or empowered.

There may be something tangible that has relaxing or empowering associations for you, so that when you see, touch, or think about this thing, you automatically feel relaxed, calm, and empowered.

It may be something that you can keep with you or bring into your environment in stressful situations. Or you may just think about it, and find that the vivid thought of the item automatically helps you feel relaxed, calm, and empowered.

For some people, water has relaxing associations. The sight, sound, touch, taste, or thought of water could be relaxing. If water has relaxing associations for you, you can potentially go to the beach to relax, make sure you have a bottle of water with you in stressful situations, or just think about water when you need to relax.

You may have received a gift from a loved one and that gift may have an automatic relaxing, calming, or empowering impact when you think about, see, or feel the touch of that item. The gift may be a necklace, a baseball cap, or anything special to you.

You may have another item that has relaxing, calming, and empowering associations for you. You can use the sight, feel, or thought of the item to bring you automatic feelings of relaxation and empowerment.

Examples of things that may be helpful to have with you or think about in stressful situations:

- Water
- A worry stone
- Gift from a loved one
- Childhood stuffed animal
- Fidget ring
- Necklace or other jewelry
- Something that represents a person, place, or animal with positive associations for you
- An object related to an activity you find calming or empowering

As with a happy place, what you're going for is something that is grounding and counters the stress you're feeling. It might be calming and relaxing, or it may be something that helps you feel more self-confident and empowered.

What might work as a relaxing or empowering thing? List some ideas of things that might help you feel relaxed, calm, self-confident, and/or empowered when you're stressed.

5. Put your thumb and finger together.

The fifth relaxation tool is putting the tips of your thumb and finger together. You can use any of your fingers along with your thumb. You can use your right hand or left hand, whichever you prefer. Or, you can use both hands.

You may recognize this position as one used in yoga and meditation for centuries. The tips of your fingers and thumb are reflexology brain points. Touching these points can be automatically relaxing and calming. And, with practice, you can reinforce and optimize the relaxation response.

One of the things that I love about this relaxation technique is that you can do it discretely anytime, with your hands down to your sides, in your lap, or in your pockets.

Practicing the relaxation techniques makes them more available when you need them in stressful situations.

Reminder: Use whichever of the relaxation techniques work for you.

You can practice using the anti-anxiety relaxation skills any time you have a few minutes:

1. Sit comfortably and close your eyes.

2. Take a couple of deep breaths.

3. Check to see if there is a word or phrase that would help you feel relaxed or empowered.

4. Check to see if you have a "happy place." If you do, vividly imagine being in your "happy place." Notice the sights, sounds, and smells associated with it. Notice what it feels like physically and emotionally.

5. Check to see if there is an item that has relaxing or empowering associations for you. If it isn't with you when you are doing a relaxation practice, think about the item. Make the thought as vivid and multi-dimensional as possible.

6. When you feel relaxed, put your thumb and finger together. You are making a stronger and stronger association between the touch of your thumb and finger together, and an automatic relaxed empowered feeling. Immediately or soon—the simple act of putting your thumb and finger together will automatically make you feel relaxed, calm, and self-confident.

7. Whenever you are ready, open your eyes.

Preparing for stressful situations

If you anticipate that a particular situation in the future will be stressful, you can visualize experiencing that situation while using your preferred anti-anxiety relaxation techniques. Such visualizations can improve your ability to deal with the situation in a calm and empowered way.

Just as your mind can ramp up your anxiety when you vividly imagine awful scenarios, your mind can increase your confidence in a good outcome if you vividly imagine things going well.

These techniques engage your body to quickly reset your mind to a calm, grounded, logical state. You can use them to relax from a wound-up, anxious state.

Drop your shoulders

This is super simple, so it may be relatively easy to remember when you are panicky.

Mental tension often stimulates physical tension. The resulting tightening of our shoulders can confine breathing.

When you notice yourself feeling tense, drop your shoulders and pull them back so that it opens your chest. Take a couple of slow, deep breaths. (Dropping your shoulders and opening your chest often leads to an automatic breath and allows for deeper breaths.)

Heart 7 acupressure point

Acupressure is performed by applying pressure to specific points on your body. A point on your wrist, just below your hand, in line with your pinky finger, is known as *Heart 7*. It is valued as an acupressure point for its ability to relieve anxiety, depression, and insomnia.

1. Using the thumb from your opposite hand, apply gentle pressure to the Heart 7 point feeling for the small, slightly hollow spot to the outside of the tendon.

2. Continue applying gentle pressure for up to 5 minutes. (You may feel immediate calming.)

Body crossover

This one takes a minute and a half. It resets your nervous system to *calm*.

1. Sit comfortably.
2. Cross your ankles.
3. Gently clasp your hands together, intertwining your fingers.
4. Place your clasped hands on your abdomen, having your forearms also resting on your body.
5. Sit like this for a minute and a half. You can do this with your eyes open or shut. You can focus on your breathing if you like, but it isn't necessary.

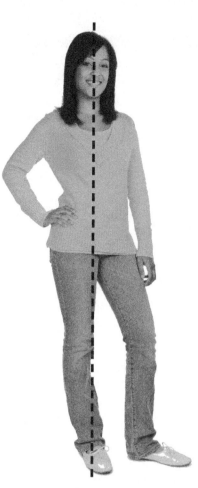

Crossing the midline

When we are anxious, our mind tends to be stuck in a closed non-creative state. Crossing the midline (the imaginary line running from your head to your feet down the center of your body) helps your brain shift to a more open creative problem-solving state.

There are many activities that can be used to cross the midline.

- Toss a ball or other object from one hand to the other across the midline.

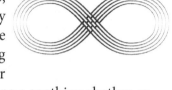

- Draw a large imaginary sideways 8, or infinity sign, in front of your body in the air with your finger (about the width of your body) while crossing your midline. Trace over it four or more times. Experiment with creating a soothing rhythm as you trace the figure. You can also pattern your breath to the tracing movement.

- Give yourself a hug. Place your left hand on your right shoulder and your right hand on your left shoulder. Take slow, deep breaths. Hold the pose as long as you like. Experiment to discover if you have a preference for which arm is crossed over first: left arm over to your right side, or vice versa.

3-3-3

This technique uses your senses to reset your mind.

1. Take a couple of slow, deep breaths.
2. Name 3 things you **see**.
3. Name 3 sounds you **hear**.
4. **Move** 3 body parts (e.g., arm, ankle, finger).
5. Take a couple of slow, deep breaths.

Grounding Reset Techniques Practice

Experiment with the techniques to discover which ones (if any) work for you.

You can use your favorite(s) daily to give yourself a calm break if you like.
Practice makes them more available when you become panicky or anxious.

30. Relax and Reset Summary

1. The goal when you are at the higher levels of fear is to get down to concern so that you can logically figure out what you are afraid of and think through your options.

2. 5 techniques to help you relax down to concern:

   1. Take a couple of slow, deep breaths.
   2. Think of a word or phrase that helps you relax or feel empowered.
   3. Think of a "happy place."
   4. Think about, or bring with you, an item that helps you feel relaxed or empowered.
   5. Put your thumb and finger together.

3. 5 quick grounding reset techniques:

   1. Drop your shoulders
   2. Heart 7 acupressure point
   3. Body crossover
   4. Crossing the midline
   5. 3-3-3 (See. Hear. Move.)

> Relax,
> refresh,
> and
> refocus.
>
> —Lailah Gifty Akita

Part Five

Challenging
Cognitive Distortions

Don't believe everything you think.

31. What are Cognitive Distortions?

Cognitive distortions warp reality. They put a negative spin on things. That distorting spin has a negative emotional, psychological, and behavioral impact on the individual who is trapped in the distortion.

While cognitive distortions happen for everyone some of the time, people with anxiety and depression tend to get stuck in the distortions. That stuckness manifests as ruminating or dwelling on the negative thoughts. The ruminating creates a consuming whirlwind that will make you more and more stressed, nervous, worried, anxious, and panicked.

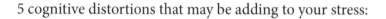

The good news is that you can train your brain to catch, check, and change this faulty thinking.

The founders of Cognitive Behavioral Therapy (CBT), Aaron Beck and David Burns, listed about a dozen cognitive distortions, which Beck described as making people create "a negative bias against themselves." I'm going to focus on five that I think are most relevant to our discussions.

5 cognitive distortions that may be adding to your stress:

1. Catastrophizing or Awfulizing
2. Overgeneralization
3. Magnification and Minimization
4. Filtering
5. Polarized thinking

It is noteworthy that a common thread with these distorted ways of thinking is a tendency to think in absolutes: *always*, *never*, *all*, and *none*.

Absolutes are almost always wrong. Absolutes make things feel worse than they really are. They will make you feel like you are globally bad, rather than seeing the isolated things you might be bad at. They make you think that things will never be better, rather than allowing you to recognize that while something might be bad now, it may be better in the future. I'll draw your attention to more absolute thinking negative impact examples as we discuss various cognitive distortions.

> Before describing individual cognitive distortions, I'm going to give you a 4-step method for calming your anxious mind so you can analyze your thoughts.

32. Thought Stopping

Anxiety can make your mind go around in circles. You can get fixated on a subject. The thoughts can become more and more upsetting and exaggerated. Your anxiety, nervousness, and worry keep escalating, and your mind gets more and more cloudy.

Remember that what we want to be able to do with fear is logically take a look at the feared thing and make a plan for how to address it. We have trouble getting that kind of mental clarity at the higher levels of fear.

PANIC (immobilizing)
ANXIETY (consuming)
NERVOUSNESS / WORRY (distracting)
CONCERN *the sweet spot

OBLIVIOUS / NUMB (avoiding)

Thought stopping is a method of getting the anxious circular thoughts to cease and desist. It helps make room for you to bring the fear down to a level of concern.

Before taking you through exercises for logically addressing cognitive distortions that contribute to stress and anxiety, I want to give you the resource of *Thought Stopping*.

Thought Stopping helps you catch yourself at ruminating and relaxes your mind and body.

4-Step Thought Stopping

1. Notice you're ruminating.

2. Stop.

3. Relax your mind.

4. Challenge the thought.

1. Notice you're ruminating.

Noticing that your mind is spinning in circles that are going nowhere constructive, and are only ramping up your angst, is the first step in the process of stopping the stress.

2. Stop

To get the mind-spinning to stop, it can help to use a cue to halt.

- You can say something to yourself like "Stop," and/or
- envision/imagine something that would help you stop, such as a stop sign, a raised hand, or a bell ringing.

The goal is to create an automatic mechanism to get your attention and help you stop the ruminating. Experiment with different attention-getting stop alerts until you find what works for you. I've had clients use everything from phrases that help them catch that they are being irrational, to imagining red traffic lights and caution tape.

3. Relax your mind.

Use any of the relaxation techniques mentioned in Chapter 28 to relax your mind.

- Taking a couple of deep breaths is a good place to start.
- A relaxing, calming, or empowering word or phrase may help reset your brain.
- Possibly think of your happy place or a calming/encouraging thing that has special meaning to you.
- If touching your finger and thumb together helps you relax, that's a great option for these circumstances.

You could also use any of the grounding resets mentioned in Chapter 29, or other relaxation techniques that work for you. Experiment to find a go-to combination.

4. Challenge the thought.

You may need to spend a few minutes doing a calming activity, but when you feel ready, it's important to take yourself to the level of concern and challenge the thought that triggered the anxious, stressed feelings.

One way to do this is to use the Catch, Check, Change sequence:

Catch. Identify the thought that came before the emotion or was spinning in your head as you ramped up.

Check. Reflect on how rational, accurate, and useful the thought is. Question whether it is based on overreactions and/or cognitive distortions.

Change. Replace the thought with something more accurate and useful.

> The next pages will walk you through the Challenge the Thought step with a variety of cognitive distortions.

33. Catastrophizing or Awfulizing

Catastrophizing (AKA *awfulizing*) is dwelling on an exaggerated worse-than-worst-case scenario. It can ramp up your anxiety even though what you are anxious about isn't really happening.

Anxiety can make your mind go around in circles. Anxious people tend to not only imagine catastrophized scenarios; they also tend to replay them over and over. The anxiety can grow and grow as the scary thoughts replay over and over.

If you think about something over and over, you will have the same emotional response as if it is happening over and over. Fear can grow bigger and bigger as you imagine awful possibilities. You can blow something up in your mind to catastrophic proportions creating a fear mushroom cloud.

Losing a job because your company downsized is scary. Vividly imagining never working again is catastrophizing. When you catastrophize, you vividly imagine devastation rather than pulling yourself back to a more realistic picture and formulating how to cope with a realistic possibility.

One way that catastrophizing shows up is in absolutes: *always, never, all, none.* Negative things feel much worse if they "always" happen versus they "sometimes" happen. Your partner always running late is worse than if they sometimes run late. "Never" is worse than "now." "I'll never have a job again" is worse than "I don't have a job right now."

Anyone may have moments when they fear the worst, but getting stuck in that position can result in chronic stress and/or a fear-drenched inability to act. It can also harm relationships. If you vividly imagine your partner doing an imaginary awful thing over and over, it will feel like your partner is awful—even if he or she has not done the thing you are imagining at all! Your anger can then reach the same level as it would if they really did that awful thing over and over.

To check for catastrophizing/awfulizing, when you catch yourself ruminating, ask yourself:

- "Is this awful thing I'm dwelling on realistic?"
- "Is this really a worst-case scenario I'm thinking about, or is it worse-than-worst case?"
- "What's the evidence that supports, or goes against, this being realistic?"

To change the distorted thought, ask yourself:

- "What would be a more helpful, accurate thought?"
- "What is a realistic scenario?"
- "What are my options for dealing with a realistic scenario?"

Reflection. Write about an experience with catastrophizing/awfulizing. (If you've had one.)

What was the situation?

What was the awfulized thought?

Was it either of these?: ☐ a worse-than-worst-case scenario   ☐ an absolute

What evidence supported the thought?	What evidence went against the thought?

Were there exceptions or possible exceptions to the awfulized scenario?

What would have been a realistic scenario?

What would have been a more helpful, accurate thought?

34. Overgeneralization

Some irrational fears are created by overgeneralizations.

As we go through life, we develop core beliefs about the world and how to function in the world. Our core beliefs may be created from faulty thinking or limited knowledge. We may be subconsciously controlled by these beliefs, and at the same time be consciously unaware of their existence.

With overgeneralizations, there is a kernel of truth to the core belief, but it gets exaggerated to cover more circumstances than are warranted. Here are a couple of examples.

Fear of spiders:

- The overgeneralized core belief: All spiders are dangerous.
- The kernel of truth: Some spiders are dangerous.

Test anxiety:

- The overgeneralized core belief: I fail tests. (Stated as an absolute.)
- The kernel of truth: It is possible to fail tests. (If you have failed a test, then the kernel of truth is, I have failed a test.)

Notice that once again, absolutes do their dirty work. *Always*, *never*, *all*, and *none* often show up as part of an overgeneralization.

Overgeneralizations drive phobias, anxiety, worry, and nervousness, and create false limitations that lock you out of seeing broader possibilities.

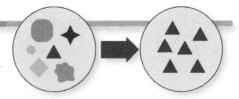

To check for overgeneralization, when you catch yourself ruminating, ask yourself:

- "Am I lumping too many things together?"
- "Am I thinking in absolutes?"
- "What's the evidence that supports, or goes against, my generalized belief?"

To change the distorted thought, ask yourself:

- "What is the kernel of truth?"
- "What would be a more helpful, accurate thought?" (It often will be connected to the kernel of truth.)

Reflection. Write about an experience with overgeneralization. (If you've had one.)

What was the situation?

What was the overgeneralized thought?

Was it either of these?: ☐ lumping too many things together   ☐ an absolute

What evidence supported the thought?

What evidence went against the thought?

What was the kernel of truth?

What would have been a more helpful, accurate thought?

35. Magnification and Minimization

With *magnification* and *minimization* you distort certain things by seeing them as bigger and grander than they really are, and other things by seeing them as smaller and less significant than they really are. This typically involves blowing up negative stuff and minimizing good stuff. This set of cognitive distortions feeds pessimism and kills optimism. That's an anxiety provoking one-two punch.

Typical things people with this cognitive distortion magnify:

- Their mistakes, weaknesses, and shortcomings
- Evidence that something isn't going well
- Potential negative outcomes
- Perceived threats

Typical things people with this cognitive distortion minimize:

- Their achievements and strengths
- Evidence of progress
- Potential positive outcomes
- Opportunities

Another interesting element of the distorted thinking in this category is that the magnification and minimization is often flipped when looking at other people. In these cases, the cognitive distorter exaggerates the achievements and strengths of others while they are minimizing their own. The resulting comparison creates an exponentially worse view of themselves and their potential for success and happiness.

To check for magnification and minimization, when you catch yourself ruminating, ask yourself:

- "Am I making a negative thing or things bigger than it is or they are?"
- "Am I making a positive thing or things smaller than it is or they are?"
- "Am I dwelling on negatives and missing positives?"
- "What's the evidence that supports, or goes against, this being realistic?"
- "Am I thinking in absolutes?"

To change the distorted thought, ask yourself:

- "What's a more realistic view of the positives and negatives?"
- "What would be a more helpful, accurate thought?"

Reflection. Write about an experience with magnifying and minimizing. (If you've had one.)

What was the situation?

What was/were the maximized or minimized thought(s)?

Which of these were involved?: ☐ magnifying ☐ minimizing ☐ absolutes

What evidence supported the thought(s)?	What evidence went against the thought(s)?

What would have been a more realistic view of the positives and negatives?

What would have been a more helpful, accurate thought?

36. Filtering

The cognitive distortion of *filtering* is a selective filter that filters out the positive things that happen and keeps the negative things.

You need some positive chips in the bank to sustain you through stress, but filtering won't allow you to retain feel-good chips that come your way, so your account has no reserves to call on.

With this distortion, hundreds of good things that happen go unnoticed, but one bad thing that happens, even if it is relatively small, consumes your attention and thoughts. Hundreds of pieces of evidence that you are safe are not retained, but one piece of evidence that there is a threat, even if it is minuscule, grabs your attention and sets off anxiety.

Filtering example: You give a well-prepared presentation. You have researched the topic and have created an interesting slide show that works with no glitches. Most of the audience is paying attention and engages with you and the material. You notice one person texting on their phone. After the presentation, many people give you positive feedback. No one gives you negative feedback. You anxiously obsess over why that one texting person wasn't interested enough in you and the presentation. You feel like the presentation was a failure.

To counter the filtering distortion:

- Allow yourself to acknowledge the negative of a situation, but don't focus on it to the exclusion of the positive.
- Practice forcing yourself to acknowledge the positive aspects of things.
- Lists may help. List the negatives and positives of situations, pushing yourself to see how many positives you can find.
- Make a positive plan to address legitimate concerns.

To check for filtering, when you catch yourself ruminating, ask yourself:

- "Am I obsessing over a negative, while ignoring positives?"
- "Am I thinking in absolutes?"
- "What's the evidence that supports, or goes against, my filtered belief?"

To change the distorted thought, ask yourself:

- "What's a more realistic view of the positives and negatives?"
- "What would be a more helpful, accurate thought?"

Reflection. Write about an experience with filtering. (If you've had one.)

What was the situation?

What was/were the filtered thought(s)?

Did the filtering involve either of these?: ☐ an absolute ☐ multiple absolutes

What evidence supported the thought(s)?

What evidence went against the thought(s)?

What were the positives that you filtered out at the time?

What would have been a more helpful, accurate thought?

37. Polarized Thinking

Polarized thinking is black-or-white, all-or-nothing, dichotomous thinking. The "di" in dichotomous means two. With dichotomous thinking, there are only two options.

Dichotomous, polarized thinking is not a very real way of viewing the world. Most things, in reality, have more than two options. Most situations have a whole continuum of possibilities between the two polar opposites.

Even if we take black and white as the epitome of polarized thinking, most of what we label black and white isn't 100% black or 100% white. Most of what we call black and white would actually fall somewhere within the continuum that represents the mixture of each. And there is the whole gray scale in between that is the combination of different degrees of black and white.

Absolutes—*always, never, all, none*—are very much alive in polarized, all-or-nothing thinking.

One of the ways polarized thinking leads to trouble is that it only allows for two possibilities: "absolutely right" and "absolutely wrong." This stimulates a lot of anxiety. You don't want to do the wrong thing, but the only way to not do the wrong thing is to do it perfectly right, and what's the chance you'll get it perfectly right?

Polarized thinking can drive you to:

- See yourself, other people, and things as either all good or all bad
- Be overly attached to your opinion as the only right opinion
- Have difficulty formulating an opinion out of fear that it will be wrong
- Be overly attached to your way of doing things as the only right way
- Have difficulty doing things because you don't want to do them wrong
- Obsessively dwell on looming decisions
- Procrastinate in situations that require choices
- Keep making the decision of no-decision
- Leave decisions up to other people (This has lots of downsides, including that those people can get tired of having to carry the weight of all the decision-making.)
- Control decisions so that they are "right"
- Fear change
- Avoid healthy risk (And the simplest of things can end up feeling like a big risk.)

Notice that some of the items on the above list are polar opposites of each other. This cognitive distortion can show up in different people in different ways, or within one person in different ways. The common denominator, however, is that the thoughts and behaviors are on extreme ends of the continuum of possibilities.

Debunking the polarized thinking right/wrong trap

Let's say that you have to decide where to go to college, and you notice you are worrying that you will either:

a. pick the right college and degree leading to happiness and success, or

b. make the wrong choice and be doomed.

What possible results could be between those 2 options? Are there c, d, e . . . options?

Here are some other possibilities:

c. You make the best calculated choice given the information and experience you currently have, and you make the best of your choice, whatever it is.

d. You make the best calculated choice given the information and experience you currently have, and make another choice if it isn't working out.

e. Any number of college choices could still lead to the same end result, just from different directions.

f. It doesn't matter which college; what really matters is how you apply yourself to your studies.

g. It doesn't matter which college; what really matters is getting the degree.

Since I've been aware of the polarized thinking mind trap, I've yet to find something that genuinely only has two possible results or options. (I don't want to take an absolute stance on this, so—I'm open to the possibility of exceptions—I just haven't noticed any yet.)

To check for polarized thinking, when you catch yourself ruminating, ask yourself:

- "Am I only seeing 2 options?"
- "Am I stuck on there being one right way to handle this?"
- "Are there any exceptions or possibility of exceptions?"
- "What's the evidence that supports, or goes against, this being realistic?"
- "Am I thinking in absolutes?"

To change the distorted thought, ask yourself:

- "Are there other possibilities between the polarized opposites?"
- "What's in the shades of gray between the black and white opposites?"
- "What would be a more helpful, accurate thought?"

What was the situation?

What was/were the polarized thought(s)?

Did the polarization involve either of these?: ☐ an absolute   ☐ multiple absolutes

What evidence supported the thought(s)?	What evidence went against the thought(s)?

What might be on the continuum between the polar opposites, or other options?

What would have been a more helpful, accurate thought?

1. Cognitive distortions warp reality. They put a negative spin on things.

2. Ruminating about cognitive distortions can contribute to anxiety.

3. 5 cognitive distortions that may be adding to your stress:

    1. **Catastrophizing or Awfulizing:** dwelling on an exaggerated worse-than-worst-case scenario

    2. **Overgeneralization:** a kernel of truth gets exaggerated to cover more circumstances than are warranted

    3. **Magnification and Minimization:** blowing up negative stuff and minimizing good stuff

    4. **Filtering:** a selective filter filters out the positive things that happen and keeps the negative things

    5. **Polarized Thinking:** black-or-white, all-or-nothing, dichotomous thinking

4. A common thread with these distortions is a tendency to think in absolutes:

    always • never • all • none

5. Absolutes are almost always wrong.

6. 4-Step Thought Stopping can interrupt anxious ruminating.

    1. Notice you're ruminating.
    2. Stop.
    3. Relax your mind.
    4. Challenge the thought. (Catch. Check. Change.)

Part Six

Anxiety-Reducing Mindset

"Life is 10 percent what happens to us
and 90 percent how we respond to it."

—Charles Swindoll

39. Anxiety-Reducing Mindset Overview

Sometimes without knowing it—or knowing how to change it if we do see it—aspects of our approach to life are contributing to our anxiety. These chapters provide small to big (and small that have a big impact) tips for a stress-busting mindset.

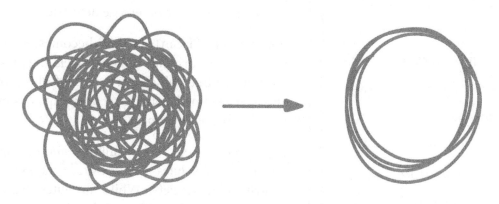

This part of the workbook covers many topics. Some will be relatable for you, and others won't. For example, there are chapters on perfectionism and procrastination. Not all people with anxiety are perfectionistic or procrastinate, but perfectionists and procrastinators tend to be anxious. For some anxious people, these chapters will be very important. For others, they won't be relevant.

Use the pieces that are a fit for you.

What's included in Part Six

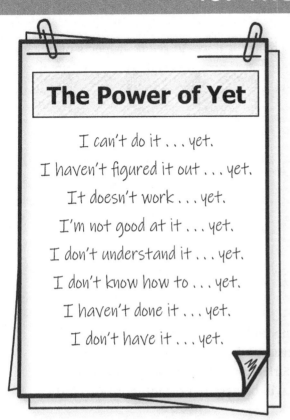

The Power of Yet

I can't do it . . . yet.

I haven't figured it out . . . yet.

It doesn't work . . . yet.

I'm not good at it . . . yet.

I don't understand it . . . yet.

I don't know how to . . . yet.

I haven't done it . . . yet.

I don't have it . . . yet.

Based on the growth mindset research of Professor Carol Dweck, *The Power of Yet* is a simple, encouraging, and calming philosophy that is easy to remember and put into action. You just add the word *yet* to the end of sentences that are otherwise defeatist.

For example, "I can't do this" becomes "I can't do this yet." The original sentence feels hopeless and absolute. Both of which can result in feeling stressed and overwhelmed. Adding *yet* opens up possibilities. It makes room for hope.

As I mentioned when talking about cognitive distortions, absolutes—*all, none, always, never*—can contribute to anxiety. While absolutes are almost always wrong, they often make things feel worse than is really warranted. The absoluteness isn't always vocalized. Sometimes it is implied. "I can't do this" can contain an implied "ever" and "at all": "I'll never be able to do this at all."

Create your own "yet" sentences for personal challenges.

You can take the Power of Yet a step further by making a plan to address the identified issue (e.g., "I can't do it yet": make a plan to help you be able to do "it"). I talk about how to make a plan in Chapter 42. Work the Problem.

41. Look for the Silver Lining

The silver lining is something good connected to a challenge or difficult situation. I'm not willing to say that there's always a silver lining to bad things—since that would be an absolute—but there is often a silver lining to bad things. It could be a positive outcome to the situation, learning potential presented by the situation, positive side effect, or protection from an unforeseen negative consequence.

Looking for the silver lining isn't about pretending everything is wonderful. It's about not losing sight of the positive potential in negative events. It can help break the anxious ruminating spiral by making you step back and reframe the situation.

Myriam Mongrain, Ph.D. of the Greater Good Science Center, UC Berkeley, suggests that looking for negative experiences' silver lining "is a key component of optimism, which research links to lower rates of depression, a better ability to cope with stress, and more relationship satisfaction, among other benefits."

Sometimes you can see a silver lining if you look for it while you're dealing with the difficult thing. Sometimes you can only see it later. Having a practice of looking for the silver lining can build your trust that even if you can't see how now, things will be OK, and maybe good, or even great.

Finding the silver lining example

Challenging situation: Not getting a job you wanted

Potential silver linings: It turns out it was a lousy job. Your current job decides to give you a raise, and you liked the job but not the amount you had been getting paid. The interview process adds to your experience for being better at your next interview. Your dream job pops up on a job board two weeks later. It points out weakness in skills or knowledge that you could work on.

> **Silver Lining Reflection: Past.** Think of a time when you thought something was all bad and terrible, but it turned out to have some positive aspect or outcome.

What was that situation?

What was/were the silver lining(s)?

Silver Lining Reflection: Present. Think of a situation that you currently think is awful or worry will be awful.

What is the situation?

What are some potential silver lining(s)?

_____

_____

_____

Silver Lining Reflection: Future. Use these sections to work through difficult situations in the future to see the potential silver lining(s).

What is the situation?

What are some potential silver lining(s)?

_____

_____

_____

What is the situation?

What are some potential silver lining(s)?

_____

_____

_____

42. Work the Problem

Anxiety, nervousness, or worry might be stimulated by a problem, such as needing a job, having to pass a test, or not knowing what to have for dinner. Bringing the higher levels of fear down to concern allows you to work the problem step by step.

3+ Steps for Problem Solving

(Note: I explain this process more fully in *A quick look at Consultation: Simple Powerful Tips for Collaborative Problem Solving, Decision Making, and Resolving Conflict* available on Amazon and annsilvers.com.)

1. Gather **knowledge**:

    ➲ Find out the facts
    ➲ Identify related values (including your feelings)

2. Create a **vision** of what to do:

    ➲ Brainstorm possible solutions (get creative with possible solutions before picking them apart)
    ➲ Analyze the pros and cons of the various ideas
    ➲ Choose a solution

3. **Act** on the decision:

    ➲ Break the solution down into doable action steps
    ➲ Decide who'll do what by when
    ➲ Take the steps one by one

➕ **Reflect** on how it's working:

    ➲ Notice what's working and what's not working

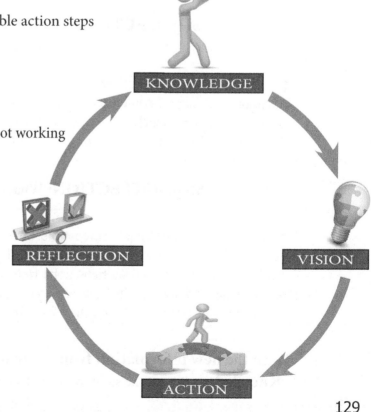

With the new understanding of the situation from reflection (the + step), you are back at Step 1 with new knowledge, and you can go through the steps again.

You get to experiment, learn from doing, and use that learning to make adjustments. It's OK to not get it "right" the first time. Finding out what doesn't work is information.

Working the problem example.

What is the problem?

I've got a big project due

Step 1. KNOWLEDGE: What are some facts and values related to the problem?

- I really need to do well on this project
- I have 3 weeks (including weekdays and 3 weekends) to get it done
- I feel OK with giving it 2 out of 3 weekends
- I can ask Evie for help
- I also have to get my other work done
- I tend to burn through time playing video games

Step 2. VISION: Brainstorm possible solutions. Then analyze ideas & choose solution(s).

2A Brainstorm possible solutions.	2B. Analyze ideas & choose solution(s).
1. ask Evie for help	1. ask Evie for help
2. do it all myself	2. ~~do it all myself~~ (Evie definitely could be helpful)
3. use the 1st weekend to get ahead	3. use the 1st weekend to get ahead
4. play 1st weekend	4. ~~play 1st weekend~~ (better to get ahead)
5. limit video game time	5. limit video game time (limit to 1 hr/day)
6. list steps for completing	6. list steps for completing

Step 3. ACTION: Make a plan and put it into action

Plan
1. talk to Evie about helping me
2. figure out how I can best use Evie's help
3. figure out how much I have to get through each day
4. focus on the project -- make sure I stick to video game limit 1 hr/day

+ Step. REFLECTION: What's working and not working?

- I contacted Evie: she doesn't have time to help me until next weekend
- I've identified 2 problem areas that she could help me with
- I divided the project into 5 sections with timelines (can do the 1st two sections myself)
- I'm half way through the 1st section (slightly behind schedule)
- I was doing well with my video game limit but blew it yesterday

With the new information from your Reflection you are back at Step 1, Knowledge. Repeat the steps as needed so you can adjust the vision and/or plan.

Practice working the problem. (You may need more room than there is on this page. Use the lined Additional Reflections pages at the back of the workbook for overflow.)

What problem would you like to take through the steps?

Step 1. KNOWLEDGE: What are some facts and values related to the problem?

Step 2. VISION: Brainstorm possible solutions. Then analyze ideas & choose solution(s).

Step 3. ACTION: Make a plan and put it into action.

+ Step. REFLECTION: What's working and not working?

With the new information from your Reflection you are back at Step 1, Knowledge. Repeat the steps as needed so you can adjust the vision and/or plan.

What you say when you are talking to yourself matters.

You can be your own worst enemy. Generalized, absolute, critical messages you say to yourself can rev up your stress, hold you back, and take you down!

Negative self-talk examples:

- "You're stupid."
- "You can't do anything right!"
- "You're ugly."
- "What a loser."
- "You'll never amount to anything."

> 66
> Be careful
> how you are
> talking to yourself
> because
> you are listening.
>
> —Lisa M. Hayes
> 99

The messages in your head may be generated from low self-esteem or perfectionism, or be repeats of messages voiced by parents (well-meaning or not), bullies, abusive partners . . .

All too often, parents or other adults who don't deal with their own shortcomings put them onto children. If a parent or other important adult repeatedly put you down—that was their stuff, not yours.

3 Steps for Stopping Negative Self-Talk

1. Begin to notice it.

Pay attention to what you say to yourself. Rather than push it away, bring it up to full awareness and hear the message clearly. Possibly write it down so you've really got it.

2. Counter the message.

The phrase "Reality Check" has worked for me as a signal to counter negative self-talk. That may work for you too. Whether or not you use that signal, you want to challenge the message and provide yourself with evidence to the contrary. It may be helpful to write out the evidence.

3. Replace negative with positive.

Replace the negative message with its positive counterpart. "You're stupid" can be replaced with positive self-talk examples like "You're not stupid," "You're smart," "You can do this," "Academics aren't your thing, but there's more to smart than school grades," or something else that empowers you.

Reflection. Write about your negative self-talk. (If you have negative self-talk).

What are some negative messages about yourself that you hear in your head?

Pick one to work on now.

Where did the message come from?

How has the message gotten in your way?

_____

_____

_____

_____

What evidence goes against the message?

_____

_____

_____

_____

What could be a positive replacement message?

Visualize catching the negative message

Sit comfortably. Close your eyes. Take a couple of slow, deep breaths. Visualize catching the negative message in the future, countering it, and replacing it with a positive message. Experiment to discover what works for you. When you're ready, open your eyes.

44. Positive Affirmations

Positive affirmation statements can be used to start your day and throughout your day to boost your self-confidence, motivation, and inspiration. They can remind you how you want to be, help you change for the better, calm and relax your anxiety naturally, and cheer you on through challenges big and small.

Affirmations affect your subconscious and conscious mind, especially when repeated. They can impact your emotions, behavior, and attitude. They can also influence how you see the world around you. Even if you don't start out believing self-affirming statements—fake it until you can make it.

Example affirmations

1. I've got this.
2. This is tough, but I am tougher.
3. With each breath, I breathe in healing. With each breath, I feel calmer, more relaxed, more self-confident.
4. I strive to change the things that I can change and accept the things that I cannot change.
5. My emotional pain, stress, and discomfort is released and washed away.
6. I act with courage while I feel fear. I am capable, strong, and resilient.
7. I feel relaxed, calm, and empowered as I go through my day.
8. Each day, I grow in confidence in my ability to deal with challenging situations in relaxed, calm, and clearheaded ways.
9. It is easier and easier to reduce anxiety to a healthy level of concern.
10. Stress flows out of me, replaced by a refreshing, calm, secure feeling.

Create some positive affirmations to experiment with.

45. Try is Not a Four-Letter Word

I get it that many people say that "try" is a bad thing—that you shouldn't say you will try to do something. That's terrible advice.

I've had many anxiety clients who have had it drilled into them by their parents or others with a mantra of "Don't say you'll try!"

I see this anti-trying ideology as illogical and damaging.

A negative side effect of the trying-is-bad philosophy is that many people who adopt it are riddled with anxiety and stress that stifles them from trying to achieve, trying new things, trying things that haven't resulted in declared successes in the past . . . And if they do try, they are drained by anxiety that accompanies the trying.

> " Anything worth doing is worth doing poorly until you learn to do it well.
>
> —Steve Brown "

Trying is a good thing. You can't accomplish anything unless you try to accomplish it. And you can't know if you can do something unless you try to do it.

If I didn't try to write this book, this book would not have been written. Gold medal athletes can't win their medal the first day they begin a sport. They keep trying to get better, hoping they will reach their goal. There are only so many gold medals. Some of those who try for them get there, and many more don't. For those who don't get the big prize, there's still plenty to be learned and gained by the trying.

Reflection. Do these sections if you've had a negative view of trying.

In the past, what messages have you received about trying?

Write a positive affirmation to help you be OK with trying.

135

46. Stretch Your Comfort Zone

We each have a comfort zone made up of those things we are used to. It is natural to experience fear whenever you consider doing something outside your comfort zone.

scary thing outside comfort zone

If you wait for the fear to subside before doing something you're not used to, you'll never do it. The fear can only go away when experience makes the object of the fear part of your comfort zone. You have to decide to go ahead and do it while feeling fear. In that way, you **stretch** your comfort zone to include the thing you previously feared. Then you can do it with more confidence.

I think that *comfort zones* would be more correctly called *familiar zones* because those things that we are used to may be comfortable for their familiarity and yet uncomfortable for their destructiveness. A person who grew up emotionally abused and is now in an emotionally abusive relationship may fear leaving because abusive experiences are familiar and somehow "comfortable," at the same time that they are uncomfortable for obvious reasons.

> Whenever we take a chance and enter unfamiliar territory or put ourselves into the world in a new way, we experience fear. Very often this fear keeps us from moving ahead in our lives.
>
> —Susan Jeffers, *Feel the Fear and Do It Anyway*

A couple of points to remember for stretching your comfort zone

1. Assess for true danger.

It's important to assess that the feared thing is not truly dangerous to yourself or others before deciding to go ahead and do it while feeling the fear.

For example, fear is supposed to stop you from running out in front of a truck—don't feel the fear and do it anyway. But speaking in front of your office mates at a meeting may be scary though not dangerous, and you would do well to go ahead while you experience the fear, so that you can stretch your familiar zone and become more comfortable with speaking to the group.

2. Break it down into doable steps.

To slowly stretch your comfort zone, break the scary thing down into doable steps. Something that is overwhelming can be made less scary by focusing on one step at a time. Figure out what the first step is in a sequence that will eventually lead to the accomplishment of a goal. Focus on the first step. Then move on to the next, and the next.

Stretching Your Comfort Zone Challenge

What is fear stopping you from doing? Pick one comfort-zone-stretching goal to work on.

Analyze the fear. What are you afraid could happen if you do this thing?

What could help you do this scary thing?

Break the goal down into steps. Keep breaking down the steps toward reaching your goal until you get to a doable first step.

What's a doable first step?

What would help you do that step?

Make a plan to take the step.

Monitor your progress. Celebrate successfully completing the step or analyze what has gotten in the way. Repeat with the next doable step.

Perfectionism creates anxiety. Not all people who have anxiety are perfectionists, but many people who are perfectionists have anxiety. Perfectionism is a tough taskmaster. The truth is . . . you can't be perfect. Other people can't be perfect. Things can't go perfectly. Perfectionists are chronically frustrated, disappointed, overwhelmed, and anxious.

Excellence is a worthy goal. Perfection is not. Here's a look at the excellence continuum:

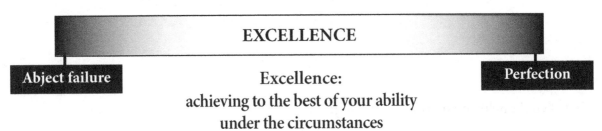

EXCELLENCE

Abject failure

**Excellence:
achieving to the best of your ability
under the circumstances**

Perfection

In Chapter 37, we talked about the cognitive distortion of polarized, dichotomous thinking: seeing only two options for things. Polarized, dichotomous thinkers might think that if they don't want to be one thing—then they have to be its opposite (because there are only two options). If someone only sees the ends of the excellence continuum, they think that being anything less than perfect means they are an abject failure.

In reality, both ends of the continuum are unhealthy. Healthy lies somewhere in the middle. This middle zone isn't a tiny pivot point you're aiming for. It's a big zone. It allows for flexibility. Sometimes the healthy use of excellence is toward the higher end of the continuum, sometimes toward the lower end. It can move around with changing priorities and different circumstances.

The perfection end of the continuum could have many labels: unflawed • spotless • pure • untarnished • faultless • blameless • undamaged • unfaultable • irreproachable • winner

The abject failure end of the continuum could also have many labels: fatally flawed • lazy • useless • worthless • defective • pathetic • slovenly • damaged • loser

If a person feels not-good-enough, polarized thinking can drive them to perfection in an attempt to quiet the fatally flawed feeling. Everything short of perfection can pick at that wound and be intolerably painful. A person who is a perfectionist may see people who are close to them, such as their children or partner, as representative of them. They may demand perfection from family because anything short of perfection in family members stimulates the person to feel like they themselves are an abject failure.

A drive to be perfect may be related to messages received as a child, unfulfilled desire to feel lovable, a quest to settle chaos, or have other sources.

If you have anxiety and you recognize that you are perfectionistic, you may benefit from examining why you have that drive and consider adjusting your goals to put you in the healthy excellence zone between the polar opposites.

Challenging Your Perfectionism. Do these sections if you tend to be perfectionistic.

What are some things that you expect to be perfect or to be done perfectly? (e.g., being on time, something specific you demand be done the "right way," your appearance, etc.)

Choose one thing that you are perfectionistic about to work on processing. (For the rest of this exercise, we'll refer to it as "this thing.")

What contributes to you having perfectionistic drive regarding this thing?

What are some of the costs or downsides to being perfectionistic about this thing?

What would a reasonable level of excellence look like for this thing when you take into account other priorities and circumstances?

Experiment with doing this thing at an imperfect reasonable level of excellence and write about your experience.

_____

_____

_____

_____

48. Let Go of Stuff Outside Your Control

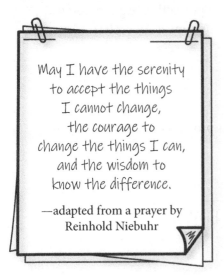

May I have the serenity to accept the things I cannot change, the courage to change the things I can, and the wisdom to know the difference.

—adapted from a prayer by Reinhold Niebuhr

If you have a drive to be in control, you probably get anxious, nervous, or worried when things aren't in your control. But not much is really within your control.

There are two good reasons the serenity prayer has been so popular for so long: lots of people suffer from trying to control things outside their control, and people feel better when they figure out how to let go of stuff that is outside their control.

The concept of owning your stuff and letting others own theirs that I talked about in Chapter 17 can be a big assist in helping you let go of what's outside your control. Own your stuff and let other people own theirs.

Outside Your Control

Other people's wants

Other people's opinions

Other people's behaviors

Other people's reactions

Within Your Control

→ Your thoughts
→ Your feelings
→ Your attitude
→ Your words
→ Your actions
→ Your reactions
→ Your behaviors
→ Your opinions
→ Your wants

Other people's thoughts

Other people's feelings

Other people's attitude

Other people's words

Other people's actions

It is important to care about yourself, your family, friends, community, and world. It is important to do what you can with what you have so that you can make a positive impact. It is also important to not be riddled with anxiety, worry, and nervousness about the outcomes of your efforts or those things outside of your sphere of influence.

Reflection. The previous diagram labels general things within and outside your control. What are some specific things that are within your control and outside your control?

Outside My Control

Within My Control

What could help reduce your anxiety, nervousness, or worry over things outside your control?

_____

_____

_____

_____

_____

49. Break Through Fear by Breaking It Down

One way to break through fear that is based on the cognitive distortion of overgeneralization (such as fear of flying, spiders, public speaking, or other phobias) is by breaking down the feared thing into steps or parts, and then reducing or eliminating your fear of each step/part. This technique, known as *desensitization*, makes you less and less sensitive to a feared thing.

Feared thing steps/parts example

For example, fear of flying might be broken down into these steps/parts:

- Looking at a flight schedule
- Buying a ticket
- Thinking about:
  - being at the ticket counter
  - going through security
  - waiting at the boarding gate
  - getting on the plane
  - other passengers getting on
  - the plane's door closing
  - takeoff
  - the flight
  - turbulence
  - landing
- Actually experiencing each of the activities on the "thinking about" list above

The desensitization process

Note: I'll refer to steps/parts as "steps" for the rest of our discussion and the exercise.

List the steps related to your feared thing, then rank each step from least scary to most scary.

Starting with the least scary step:

- Consider what would help you cope with this one step (e.g., having someone supportive with you, listening to relaxing music, or using the relaxation or grounding reset techniques listed in Part Four: How to Relax and Reset).
- Visualize taking the step and using the coping strategies to help you relax if you begin to feel anxious. (You may need to do the visualization several times on different occasions until the fear is greatly reduced or eliminated.)

When you feel ready, either actually do the step while using your coping strategies or move on to visualize coping with the next step on your scary list.

Take it one step at a time. Eventually, the thing isn't overwhelmingly scary anymore.

Note: I have found that many phobia clients also benefit from uncovering the root cause(s) of the phobia and healing the old wound(s). Many times, it isn't one technique that greatly reduces an individual's anxiety, but rather a combination of approaches. There are many ways to come at an issue. Each provides a piece of the healing puzzle.

Break down your fear. Do this exercise if you have a fear that could benefit from desensitization.

What is the fear?

Break the fear into steps and then rank the steps from least scary to most scary.

Fear Rank	STEP

What could help you cope with taking the least scary step?

Visualize taking the step

Sit comfortably. Close your eyes. Take a couple of slow, deep breaths.
Visualize taking the least scary step while using your coping strategies.
Experiment to discover what works for you. When you're ready, open your eyes.

Repeat visualization, do it in real life, or move on to the next step.

Depending on how much anxiety relief you got with your visualization and how you want to approach the steps, either:

- repeat the visualization in the future,
- do the step in real life while using your coping strategies, or
- move on to visualize coping with the next step in your fear ranking.

50. Stop Procrastination Now

Procrastination is putting off tasks that would be better done sooner. The *better* might be that you or someone else would feel better if the tasks were done sooner, or it might be that the job would be done better, or that your life would be better in some way. People who procrastinate don't necessarily procrastinate about everything. They may put off working on some deadlines and projects, while they tackle other things in a more timely way.

Procrastination can create anxiety.

It's not hard to see that leaving things until the last minute, or until it's too late to do a good job, or too late to get it done at all—can cause stress and anxiety. The entire time between a deadline being set, or a to-do being acknowledged, and the accomplishment of the task may be stressful, or stress can appear as the deadline approaches. Plus, the repercussions of not getting things done that needed to be done can create anxiety.

Anxiety can create procrastination.

The mental, emotional, and physical drain of anxiety can get in the way of focusing on what needs to get done and systematically taking the steps to achieve goals and deadlines. Also, fears that are the basis of anxiety can drive procrastination. The fear could be fear of failure or success, or it could be connected to trying to accomplish a particular goal. You could put off booking a flight because you are afraid of flying, procrastinate about paying bills because you're afraid you don't have enough money to pay them all, or drag your feet on responding to an invitation because of social anxiety.

Steps to stop procrastination and get things done

1. Analyze for what hurts and helps.

What could get in the way of you accomplishing this thing?
What could help?

2. Break the task down into doable steps.

Keep breaking down the task until you get to a small doable step. Set a time deadline for getting the step done.

3. Do a step.

If you are not getting around to doing the step, check to see if the task needs to be broken down further, and ask yourself the Step 1 questions.

4. Celebrate and repeat.

Give yourself a pat on the back for progress. (Yeah you!) Then tackle the next step.

Stop procrastination challenge. Do these sections if you tend to procrastinate.

What is something that you tend to procrastinate about or are currently procrastinating about?

What could get in the way of accomplishing this thing?

What could help you do this thing?

Break the task/goal down into steps. Keep breaking down the steps toward reaching your goal until you get to a doable first step.

What's a doable first step?

What would help you do that step?

Make a plan to take the step.

Monitor your progress. Celebrate successfully completing the step, or analyze what has gotten in the way. Repeat with the next doable step.

51. Beware of Taking on Others' Anxiety

Sometimes, we take on other people's emotional overflow like a sponge absorbing a toxic spill. The result can be that you now have a container full of emotion that doesn't belong to you. You can feel overwhelmed by their stuff and not have the room you need for processing your own stuff.

People can have the mistaken idea that empathy involves taking on other people's pain. It doesn't. Being supportive and empathetic involves acknowledging other people's pain and seeking to understand it. It includes giving them an opportunity to unburden themselves by having room to express their pain. But that doesn't include you taking it on.

If you notice yourself taking on other people's emotional pain, it may be helpful to imagine some sort of device that would protect you. The goal is that the other person gets the benefit of letting go of their pain, but you don't get weighed down by it.

Here are two ways of diverting other people's pain:

1. **An imaginary container.** I picked up this technique from a professor when I was a student working on my Masters in Counseling. When someone is giving off emotional pain, you imagine it being directed into a container. Mine is a cement box with a small slit between the lid and box. Emotions can go into the box through the slit but can't get back out. The box is an incinerator. It is invisible. And it defies gravity. I have rarely needed to use it, but when I have, I feel the relief of stopping an influx of pain. Many of my clients have come up with their own container ideas: jars, baskets, etc.

2. **An imaginary protective device.** Some people imagine a protective device like a shield, bubble, or armor. The goal is to stop the bad but let in the good, stop the emotional pain but let in the rest.

Reflection. Do this exercise if you tend to take on other people's pain.

If you tend to take on other people's pain, what might help you stop doing that?

Experiment with using your selected method for not taking on other people's pain and write about your experience.

146

52. Savor the Feel-Good

Happiness is a skill. Unfortunately, many people lack this skill. It may be that they just haven't been taught how to be happy, or it may be that it was actively stifled.

In Part One: Understanding Emotions, I talked about the tendency to have the release valves stuck open on the feel-good emotion containers. We need to learn how to close down those release valves long enough to savor the feel-good and be nourished by it.

Savoring the happy, comfortable emotions is the equivalent of putting some chips in the bank. Having those chips in the bank helps us be more resilient in dealing with situations that cause stress. It gives us a positive reserve to draw on.

Increasing My Happiness Quotient: Silver Lining Joy Journal and Workbook offers daily exercises for building the skill of happiness and opportunities for noting small and large sources of joy. That workbook/journal could make a great balancer to the work you are doing in this workbook/journal. *Building Skills to Uplevel Life: Silver Lining Emotional Intelligence Workbook* also has a lot of guidance for up-regulating feel-good emotions.

Becoming more attentive to moments of happiness is a great start at boosting your happiness reserves. "I" messages made with comfortable emotions can help. Taking the time to savor the feel-good also helps.

Feel-good reflection. Think of a time you were happy. (It can be just a moment of happiness. It doesn't have to be big.)

Describe the situation/circumstances and your experience.

On the next page, check the emotions on the comfortable emotions list that you feel or felt regarding the situation, and complete the related "I" messages.

- ☐ Accepted
- ☐ Acknowledged
- ☐ Amused
- ☐ Appreciated
- ☐ Attracted
- ☐ Attractive
- ☐ Calm
- ☐ Capable
- ☐ Caring
- ☐ Competent
- ☐ Confident
- ☐ Connected
- ☐ Considered
- ☐ Content
- ☐ Creative
- ☐ Curious
- ☐ Delighted
- ☐ Empowered
- ☐ Encouraged
- ☐ Enthusiastic
- ☐ Excited
- ☐ Exhilarated
- ☐ Grateful
- ☐ Happy
- ☐ Hopeful
- ☐ Important
- ☐ Included
- ☐ Independent
- ☐ Inspired
- ☐ Interested
- ☐ Liberated
- ☐ Loved
- ☐ Nurtured
- ☐ Passionate
- ☐ Protected
- ☐ Proud
- ☐ Reassured
- ☐ Relaxed
- ☐ Relieved
- ☐ Respected
- ☐ Safe
- ☐ Satisfied
- ☐ Secure
- ☐ Stimulated
- ☐ Supported
- ☐ Surprised
- ☐ Trusted
- ☐ Trusting
- ☐ Understood
- ☐ Valued
- ☐ Welcome

Write "I" messages related to the situation.

I feel/felt _____

when/to/that/of/about _____

_____

_____

because _____

_____

_____

_____

I feel/felt _____

when/to/that/of/about _____

_____

_____

because _____

_____

_____

_____

Visualization

Sit comfortably and close your eyes.
Take a couple of slow, deep breaths.

Take yourself back to the happy situation.

Notice the feel-good feelings.
Breathe in that feeling as if you are breathing it in to the core of you.
From the core of you, let it spread out and fill you up.
Savor the feeling.

When you're ready, open your eyes. Smile.

1. Use the Power of Yet to overcome defeatist statements: "I can't do it . . . yet."

2. Look for the silver lining: something good connected to a challenge or difficult situation.

3. Work problems with 3+ steps for problem-solving.

4. Stop negative self-talk. Use positive affirmations.

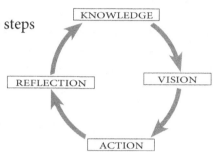

5. Trying is a good thing. You can't accomplish anything unless you try to accomplish it. And you can't know if you can do something unless you try to do it.

6. It's natural to feel fear when you consider doing something outside your comfort zone. Stretching your comfort zone involves doing the feared thing while feeling fear.

7. Perfectionists are chronically frustrated, disappointed, overwhelmed, and anxious because perfection is impossible to achieve. Strive for excellence instead.

8. To have more serenity in your life, work on things that are inside your control and let go of things outside your control.

9. For reducing or eliminating phobias, break the feared thing down into steps and desensitize it a step at a time.

10. To stop procrastinating:

    1. Analyze for what hurts and helps.

    2. Break the task down into doable steps.

    3. Do a step.

    4. Celebrate and repeat.

11. Empathy is not about taking on other people's emotional pain. Learn to acknowledge other people's feelings without absorbing them yourself.

12. Developing the skill of happiness provides some emotional chips in the bank to counterbalance challenges and increase stress resilience.

Part Seven

Stress Resilience Lifestyle

"A healthy lifestyle is the
most potent medicine at your disposal."

—Sravani Saha Nakhro

Anxiety is both a mental and physical thing. Choices about exercise, sleep, food, and activities have the potential to add to your stress load or improve your ability to deal with stress. Without knowing it, some of your lifestyle choices may be making your life harder than it needs to be and undermining your ability to cope. On the flip side, some simple changes may result in big stress resilience improvements.

Prioritizing sufficient sleep is crucial for mental well-being. The world is much easier to deal with when we've gotten some sleep. For anxious people, just talking about sleep can be anxiety-provoking. Lying awake as your mind churns about awful stuff can be torturous. I've already presented many psychological tools for interrupting anxious rumination. Now, I'll give you a dozen lifestyle tips to increase your chances for a good night's sleep.

Nourishing your body with a balanced diet also plays a crucial role in stress resilience. Avoiding excessive caffeine, alcohol, and processed foods, and focusing on consuming nutrient-rich foods, can help stabilize mood and support overall well-being. I spent three years researching and writing a book about food and supplements for anxiety. While there isn't room in this workbook to cover everything I learned through that process and included in *Feed Your Calm: Anti-Anxiety Anti-Stress Diet and Supplement Tips for Stress Resilience,* I'll pass on some highlights in Chapters 56–60.

Regularly engaging in physical exercise like walking, sports, or yoga has been shown to release endorphins, reduce stress levels, and promote resilience. Similarly, spending time outdoors and connecting with nature can have a calming and rejuvenating effect. I'll go into more detail about these and other physical approaches to anxiety relief in the upcoming chapters.

What's included in this part

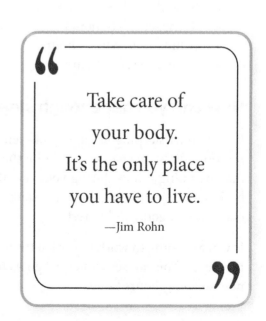

" Take care of your body. It's the only place you have to live.

—Jim Rohn "

55. The Sleep-Anxiety Connection

There's a chicken-and-egg relationship between anxiety and lack of sleep. Both impact the other. It may be difficult to tell which came first, but they create a cycle and downward spiral.

Many people who have experienced anxiety find that their sleep is disturbed by a mind that won't shut down. Some have trouble falling asleep, some wake up and can't go back to sleep, some suffer both sleep disturbances.

But it isn't just that the anxiety makes it more difficult to sleep. Difficulty sleeping also potentially makes anxiety worse. Recent research suggests that brain chemical and functional changes associated with sleep deprivation create an increase in anxiety.

So here's the challenge:

- a lack of sleep can cause anxiety, and
- anxiety can cause a lack of sleep.

Here's the good news:

- getting sufficient sleep may help reduce your anxiety.

How much sleep is enough?

The amount of sleep needed by an individual for optimal well-being varies between people and throughout a person's lifespan. The US National Sleep Foundation recommends the following daily sleep durations:

- School-aged children: 9-11 hours
- Teenagers: 8-10 hours
- Adults 18 to 64: 7-9 hours
- Adults 65+: 7-8 hours

How can you get enough sleep?

If you aren't sleeping enough now—either because anxiety is keeping you awake or for other reasons—lifestyle changes might be the key to improving your sleep quantity and quality. You may be doing things during your day that you don't realize are contributing to your mind or body's inability to slow down for sleep. There may be things that you can do to improve your chances of a good night's rest.

If you are going to work toward getting more sleep, you may want to slowly back up your sleep timetable. You can set sequential goals to get a little more sleep each night until you reach your new sleeping-hours target.

Tips for Better Sleep

1. Plan for a winding down period before bed.

Figure out how much time is needed for winding down, then calculate backward what time you need to start the winding down process so that you can get to sleep on time.

2. Be mindful of what you expose your mind to before bed.

What you expose your mind to shortly before bed can stay with you when you're trying to relax for sleep. It's best to avoid the news or media that rev up anxious thoughts.

3. Don't take your electronic devices to bed.

Aside from the potential of stimulating instead of relaxing your mind in preparation for sleep, the blue light emitted by most electronic devices has been shown to decrease melatonin. (Melatonin is a natural chemical that tells your body it's time to sleep.)

4. Stop caffeine by 3 pm or earlier.

For many people, even if they can fall asleep OK, caffeine intake late in the day results in a more disturbed sleep. Most people can eliminate caffeine's impact on their sleep by stopping intake by 3 pm, but that isn't early enough for some. A cup of coffee consumed at 10 am might get in the way of a good night's sleep. How you react to caffeine depends on your body and current conditions. (More on this in the next chapter.)

5. Don't drink alcohol before bed.

Alcohol's interference with sleep goes against conventional wisdom, but while alcohol may relax you to fall asleep, it creates a less refreshing sleep. (More on this in Chapter 57.)

6. Don't eat a big meal before bed.

Eating before bed sends your body the signal that it needs to rev up for the digestion process. This is counterproductive when you want to wind down for sleep.

7. Keep a notepad and pen by the bed.

If you keep a notepad and pen by your bed, you can use it to write down thoughts that are keeping you awake. Often writing them down releases your mind from having to remind you about the thoughts, and you are able to fall asleep.

8. Get enough exercise.

Exercise keeps your body working at its optimum—that includes sleeping well. (It may not be wise to exercise just before bed, as that could make you too energized for sleep.)

9. Listen to something relaxing.

Soothing music, white noise, or hypnosis recordings (such as my *Discover Calm, Anti-Anxiety Hypnosis,* or *Release and Refresh, Emotional Detox Hypnosis,* which are both available on annsilvers.com) can help you relax for sleep.

10. Have a relaxing bath or footbath.

Magnesium is a mineral that can relax both your body and mind. Epsom salts contain magnesium sulfate. They can be added to an evening full-body bath or footbath to help you relax for sleep. Magnesium chloride flakes can also be used this way, and they are even more potent relaxants than Epsom salts. (See Chapter 65.)

11. Drink herbal teas to relax.

There are many herbal teas that are thought to have relaxing properties. You may want to try chamomile, Valerian, or an herbal tea mixture such as Sleepy Time tea. (Chapter 60 provides more details.)

12. Use a weighted blanket.

Weighted blankets offer deep touch pressure that mimics a hug. There is promising research that weighted blankets can help you get to sleep and improve sleep quality.

Make a plan. If you have a problem getting enough sleep, make a sleep improvement plan.

What's your plan?

What could help your plan succeed?

56. Is Caffeine Amping Up Your Anxiety?

Caffeine can jack up your reaction to stress and increase nervousness, anxiety, and panic. It can make you feel on edge and wired. And it can interfere with sleep.

Caffeine is a stimulant. It can stimulate your fight-or-flight adrenal response creating the physical cascade of symptoms related to anxiety, including increased heart rate and a spike in blood sugar. (I've seen people end up in the emergency room from a panic attack brought on by a high-caffeine energy drink.)

Different people can be more or less sensitive to caffeine, and an individual may be more sensitive at different times in their life and under different circumstances. Stress may up your reaction to caffeine.

Caffeine, the sleep buster

One of the worst potential problems with anxiety is not being able to quiet your mind so you can sleep. It is painful to lie there having your mind go round in circles. And worry about not being able to sleep compounds whatever other worries are cycling through your mind, adding anxiety about not sleeping to your other anxiety.

Even if you get to sleep without trouble, caffeine can still ruin your sleep.

Caffeine can:

- make it difficult to fall asleep,
- make you restless during sleep,
- keep you stuck in a light stage of sleep,
- interrupt your sleep, and/or
- shorten the length of sleep by waking you up early.

The half-life for caffeine is approximately five hours. On average, it takes five hours for half of the caffeine consumed to be eliminated. Notice that it's only half gone in five hours. Caffeine that you consumed ten hours ago can be wrecking your sleep. It's also noteworthy that some things can extend caffeine's half-life, such as older age, smoking, pregnancy, and particular illnesses and medications. So—you might react differently to caffeine at different times in your life.

Caffeine sources

The most obvious sources of caffeine are coffee, tea, and cola, but they aren't the only sources. Some foods that have caffeine, like orange soda, may sneak up on you.

There is caffeine in:

- Coffee
- Black, white, and green tea
- Chai tea
- Iced tea
- Kombucha
- Yerba mate
- Guarana
- Cola
- Non-cola sodas like Sunkist Orange Soda, Mountain Dew, Barq's Root Beer, and A&W Cream Soda
- Chocolate
- "Energy" drinks like Red Bull, Monster, and Crystal Light Energy
- Some nootropic supplements and many workout supplements
- Some pain medications and diet pills
- Most processed foods (from granola bars to beef jerky) that have "Bang," "Boost," "Energy," or similar words in their title
- Decaffeinated coffee and tea

If you want to monitor your caffeine intake, start checking food and beverage labels to see if caffeine or caffeine sources are on the ingredients list. Sometimes the list won't include the word *caffeine*, but will say something like *green tea extract* or *guarana*.

Websites, such as Caffeine Informer (caffeineinformer.com), may help you figure out how much caffeine is in a particular food.

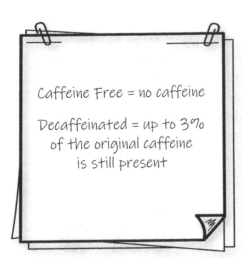

Caffeine Free = no caffeine

Decaffeinated = up to 3% of the original caffeine is still present

Caf, decaf, no caf

Decaffeinated is not the same thing as *caffeine free*.

Caffeine free has no caffeine. *Decaffeinated* coffee and tea still have caffeine in them. They have way less caffeine than their normal counterparts, but they still have caffeine.

Products that are *caffeine free*, like caffeine-free herbal teas, don't start out with caffeine and don't have caffeine added.

Decaffeinated products have to go through a process of caffeine removal because they contain caffeine in their natural state. There are several different ways to remove caffeine from coffee and tea, but none of the methods remove all of the caffeine. By law, at least 97% of the caffeine must be removed before something can be called decaffeinated, but that still leaves around 3% of the caffeine. How much caffeine remains in a particular product depends on how much it started with and the decaffeinating process used.

The most common decaffeination methods involve a solvent: either methylene chloride or ethyl acetate. There are two other decaffeination methods that do not use solvents: 1) the Swiss Water Method, employing a water-based process and commonly used for organic coffee, and 2) a newer solvent-free method utilizing CO_2 popular for very large quantities, such as decaf for grocery store chains.

Ways to cut back on caffeine

Research has linked anxiety to caffeine consumption and also to caffeine withdrawal, so if you have a big caffeine habit, quitting abruptly may not be the way to go.

There are many potential ways of cutting down on caffeine, including:

- ❑ Quit entirely
- ❑ Abruptly or gradually move back the time of day you stop consuming caffeine
- ❑ Eliminate some, but not all, of your sources of caffeine
- ❑ Consume smaller portions
- ❑ Change all or some of your drinks to decaffeinated versions
- ❑ Mix in decaffeinated portions (half caf, half decaf)
- ❑ Replace caffeine beverages with naturally caffeine-free alternatives, like herbal teas instead of black tea, or chicory root "coffee" or dandelion root tea instead of coffee
- ❑ Drink water instead (your body will thank you)

Make a plan. If caffeine might be adding to your anxiety, make a plan to reduce or stop caffeine intake.

What's your plan?

What could help your plan succeed?

57. Is Alcohol Increasing Your Anxiety?

People with anxiety can be drawn to self-medicate with alcohol. You may be drawn to overuse alcohol as a relaxation aid, or to reduce anxiety in social or performance settings.

Using alcohol to relax creates four potential problems:

1. It can lead to alcohol abuse or addiction.
2. It gets in the way of finding healthy ways to cope.
3. Alcohol has a paradoxical effect on sleep: it may help you get to sleep, but it disturbs sleep.
4. Since alcohol stresses your body, there is a shadow effect to its use that results in increased anxiety the next day.

Other ways to relax

If you are using alcohol to relax after work, before bedtime, or in social situations, that might not be all that bad for you if you are able to keep the amount in a safe usage zone. If you wander into unhealthy territory, or you're already deep into it, you may benefit from working with a therapist or support group to help you stop drinking or cut back.

If your alcohol consumption might be contributing to your anxiety, interfering with your sleep, or undermining happiness and success, you may want to experiment with other ways to relax:

- ❑ Replace the alcohol with some other drink, like herbal tea or juice with bubbly water
- ❑ Replace an alcoholic beverage that you use to mark the transition from work to not-work times of day with some other marker of the transition
- ❑ Use any of the calming activities listed throughout this workbook (e.g., Chapter 65)

Make a plan. If alcohol might be adding to your anxiety, make a plan to reduce or stop alcohol intake.

What's your plan?

What could help your plan succeed?

58. Exercise Away Stress

Physical exercise is one of many natural remedies for anxiety. It is great for keeping the muscles from harboring tension and also helps your mind and mood.

Exercise can improve your mental health and relieve stress by:

1. Helping your mind move over from your worries to focusing on the physical activity
2. Releasing feel-good endorphins
3. Reducing inflammation (research has shown a connection between inflammation and anxiety)
4. Relaxing you (during or after the exercise)
5. Improving sleep (which then, in turn, decreases anxiety and stress)
6. Helping everything in your body work better, including the organs that control stress hormones like cortisol and adrenaline
7. Helping you become more comfortable with an increased heart rate (so that when your heart rate goes up with anxiety, you don't compound the anxiety by getting anxious about your heart rate)
8. Boosting your self-confidence
9. Working the muscles that have tensed up from the stress

What's the best exercise to relieve stress and anxiety? . . . Whatever exercise you'll do.

Exercise advice commonly suggests 20 to 30 minutes most days. (Having said that, it's important to note that 5 minutes of exercise is better than zero minutes. Start where you are and work your way up to the ideal. Every bit helps.) Research shows that aerobic exercise, weight training, Tai Chi, and yoga all have the potential of reducing anxiety and relieving stress.

All exercise doesn't have to happen in a gym. The goal is to increase movement.

Ways to get more movement into your schedule without going to the gym could include:

- Going for a walk
- Taking the stairs
- Parking your car further away in the parking lot
- Cleaning the house with gusto
- Gardening
- Walking at coffee break or lunch hour
- Getting outside with the kids or the dog
- Playing soccer with your friends
- Dancing
- Hula hooping
- Jumping on a mini-trampoline

Make an exercise plan.

What time of day are you most likely to exercise?

What days of the week will most likely work to fit in movement?

What type of exercise would you like to do?

What's a good length of time for each exercise session? (Set a length of time goal for when you first begin, and then set incremental increases, until you get to your ultimate goal.)

When will you start?

What could get in the way of meeting your goal?

What could help you succeed?

Monitor your progress. Celebrate successes,
and analyze what gets in the way when you don't meet your goals.

59. Eating for Stress Resilience

I talk lots more about how what you eat impacts your mood and specific food recommendations in my book *Feed Your Calm: Anti-Anxiety Anti-Stress Diet and Supplement Tips for Stress Resilience*. I'll touch on a few points here.

My general advice for anti-stress eating is the same basic advice given for healthy eating:

1. Focus on real food
2. Eat protein throughout the day
3. Eat your vegetables
4. Have some fruit, but don't overdo it
5. Eat a variety of foods
6. Drink enough water

1. Focus on real food

Eat crap and you'll feel like crap. Processed foods come with lots of baggage that can tax your physical processes (including those called into action to deal with stress) and muck up your inner workings.

Eat natural foods. Have fun learning how to cook. Even if you have limited time for meal prep, some healthy foods are more about planning than prepping: it doesn't take much time to make a hard-boiled egg, and it takes no time to make an apple.

Eat organic and pasture-raised if and when you can. Organic foods are beneficial for what they don't have: GMOs, pesticides, and chemicals (all of which can add to your stress load). The eggs and meat from pasture-raised animals also possess nutrients that their factory-farm-raised brethren don't have.

2. Eat protein throughout the day

When Mental Health Integrative Medicine specialist and pioneer Dr. Kristen Allott is working with anxiety patients, her first area of focus is getting them to eat protein regularly throughout the day. Protein provides sustained energy rather than the spikes and dips of sugary or high-carb foods.

Dr. Allott suggests that anxiety clients eat protein every three hours during the day. If you aren't fueling your body, you are stressing it out and you'll feel stressed out. You don't expect your car to get you where you want to go without gas. Don't ask yourself to run on fumes either.

USDA dietary guidelines for protein (grams/day)
women: 46   men: 56

Protein examples (in g)
3 oz meat or fish: 15
1 large egg: 6
1/2 cup beans: 8
1/2 cup quinoa: 4

3. Eat your vegetables

Vegetables are a major source of a variety of vitamins, minerals, and bonus nutrients that help your body and brain do what they need to do.

I've heard different recommendations about the target number of vegetables per day, from five to nine. If you don't eat many vegetables now, don't focus on the higher number. Consider adding one daily serving. Add more when you are ready. Aim for at least five servings a day and then consider increasing it.

A serving is about one cup of fluffy raw salad greens or half a cup of other vegetables; some say to use your fist size as a serving. It doesn't have to be five different vegetables. If you have two cups of one non-fluffy vegetable, that is four servings.

4. Have some fruit but don't overdo it

Like vegetables, fruits offer many valuable nutrients, but be careful about overdoing it because they also contain sugar. It's a natural sugar and provides a healthy way to soothe a sweet tooth when taken in moderation, but that sugar adds up if you overdo fruit. Aim for about two servings a day, no more than four. A serving is a small apple or a half cup of berries. Eat fruit, but eat more vegetables.

Fruit & vegetable
serving sizes (in cups)

fluffy salad greens: 1
other veggies: 1/2
berries: 1/2

5. Eat a variety of foods

While there are benefits to individual foods that make them stand out for their anti-anxiety qualities, variety is important so that you get a mix of what you need. If you get too narrow of a food focus, even with relatively healthy foods, you can suffer from too much of a good thing. You need vegetables, fruits, and proteins. And you need variety within those food groups.

Mental health nutrition specialist Dr. Leslie Korn coined the phrase *brainbow* to accentuate her belief that your brain needs elements from fruits and vegetables that represent the colors of the rainbow: red, orange, yellow, green, blue, and purple.

Understandably, there may be times that you must drastically limit your choices, such as when you are on an elimination diet or dealing with a restrictive condition. Hopefully, those times are short-term.

6. Drink enough water

Your body is 50–60% water. All your organs and glands need water. Water is the vehicle that transports biochemicals throughout your body. It moves nutrients to the spots they are required. It moves toxins and reaction leftovers out of your body. If you don't take in enough water throughout the day, you hamper cellular function, and stifle your body's ability to create neurotransmitters and hormones required to deal with stress. Dehydration also stresses out your body, and that adds to your stressor load. Research has shown that even mild dehydration can cause negative changes in mood and energy, increased confusion and anxiety, and poorer sleep quality.

You get about 20% of your water requirement from food. That percentage goes up if you consume more fruits and vegetables. The rest comes more directly from liquids. Beverages that contain caffeine don't count towards your water intake because caffeine is a diuretic (it pulls water out through your kidneys). Broths in soups and non-diuretic herbal teas do count.

How much water is enough? The answer to that question varies with your activity level, heat exposure, and body size. A common guideline is the number of ounces that equals half your body weight measured in pounds.

Body weight in pounds ÷ 2 = number of ounces water

For example: 150 lbs. ÷ 2 = 75 oz.

Make a stress resilience eating plan. Considering the 6 anti-anxiety eating habits, make a plan to keep up helpful habits you have now and make helpful adjustments.

What's your plan?

What could help your plan succeed?

60. Anti-Anxiety Supplements

Supplements offer a way to boost particular nutrients individually or in mixes of several together. They also give you an opportunity to consume some herbs or plants not readily available as a food that you would prepare and eat.

Research has provided promising anti-anxiety results for a number of vitamin, mineral, fat, amino acid, probiotic, and herbal supplements. I know that supplements have helped reduce my anxiety, and I've seen dramatic improvements in anxiety clients once they begin taking some of the supplements on the list below.

In *Feed Your Calm: Anti-Anxiety Anti-Stress Diet and Supplement Tips for Stress Resilience*, I explain why certain supplements make my Top 10 list and go into detail about the benefits of each, as well as discuss recommended forms and dosage, but I'll touch on supplements quickly here as food for thought.

My Top 10 Stress Resilience Supplements

- ❑ Magnesium
- ❑ B vitamins
- ❑ Vitamin C
- ❑ Vitamin D_3
- ❑ Omega-3 Fats, EPA and DHA
- ❑ Probiotics
- ❑ Adaptogens (e.g., Ashwagandha, Maca Root, Holy Basil, Rhodiola, Schisandra, and American ginseng)
- ❑ L-Theanine
- ❑ Zinc
- ❑ Nervine herbs (e.g., Chamomile, Valerian, Passionflower, and Lemongrass)

Even natural substances can cause problems for some people some of the time. Be thoughtful about taking supplements. You can be allergic to particular herbs or have other negative reactions. It is always recommended that you consult your personal medical professionals before using supplements, especially if you have medical conditions, or you are pregnant or breastfeeding, and especially about herbs or other botanicals.

If you are on pharmaceutical drugs, check with your doctor to make sure there aren't any negative interactions between supplements you are considering and your medications. There are some online sources with lists of interactions between pharmaceuticals and supplements. The Medscape and WebMD websites, for example, have drug/supplement interaction checkers.

Tips for taking supplements:

- Quality is important. Buy supplements that are from organic or non-GMO sources whenever you can.

- Look at the back of supplement bottles to see the full list of ingredients.

- Avoid supplements with added artificial color and preservatives.

- Start new supplements one at a time in small doses. Work your way up to a full dose over a few days so you get a chance to catch any negative reaction.

- You may want to get lab tests before starting supplements, so you establish a baseline of where you are without them. (This is particularly true for vitamin D.)

You have a unique set of circumstances and exposure to physical and emotional stressors, and unless you have an identical twin, your body is different from everyone else's. Which supplements are best for you, and in what amount, is very individual.

If the possibility of using supplements to boost your stress resilience interests you, make a plan for doing more research into what might be helpful to you.

> **Using supplements.** If you choose to experiment with using supplements to calm anxiety and boost stress resilience, check off which supplements you try, and write about the results you notice.

61. Calming Essential Oils

Aromatherapy uses the smell and other properties of highly concentrated botanical essential oil extracts to make positive changes to your body and mind.

Essential oils exist in flower petals and under the surface of the leaves, bark, or peel of some plants. The fragrance is released by crushing the source part of the plant or by other extraction processes. Fragrances from the oils are released into the air, and components of the oils are absorbable through your skin.

> "Science is now confirming what has been known for centuries: essential oils have healing properties on both physical and emotional levels.
> Absorbed through the skin and via the olfactory-brain connection through inhalation, they have been considered among the most therapeutic and rejuvenating of all botanical extracts throughout the ages."
>
> —Valerie Gennari Cooksley,
> author of *Aromatherapy: Soothing Remedies to Restore, Rejuvenate and Heal*

One caution about essential oils: many of them are potentially harmful to cats and dogs. If you have pets, check online or with your vet to make sure particular oils are safe for them to be around.

Which essential oil is best for you is a personal choice and will depend in large part on how much you enjoy the scent. Some essential oils are more expensive than others to produce because they are rare, difficult to extract, or it takes a lot of the plant to create high-quality oils. For example, it takes 22 pounds of rose petals to create 5 ml (.17 ounces) of rose essential oil and 220 pounds of orange blossoms to produce 75 ml (2.5 ounces) of neroli oil. A little goes a long way with essential oils. You use just a few drops at a time. Still, you may want to try less expensive options first.

Essential oils for anxiety and stress relief

I divided the list of essential oils into an A tier (relatively inexpensive), and a B tier (effective for relieving anxiety but more expensive to produce than those in the first list).

Tier A. The relatively inexpensive ($10 to $15 per bottle of high-quality essence) essential oils that research tells us have calming effects include:

- ❏ Lavender (*L. angustifolia*)
- ❏ Lemongrass (*Cymbopogon citratus*)
- ❏ Sweet orange (*Citrus sinensis*)
- ❏ Geranium (*Pelargonium graveolens*)
- ❏ Bergamot (*Citrus bergamia*)
- ❏ Ylang Ylang (*Cananga odorata*)

Tier B. These next anti-anxiety essential oils are more expensive to produce in good quality forms ($45 or more per bottle) than the ones on the first list:

- ❑ Lemon balm (*Melissa officinalis*)
- ❑ Bitter orange, AKA neroli (*Citrus aurantium*)
- ❑ Rose (*Rose centifolia, Rose damascene*)

How to use essential oils

Pharmaceutical-grade essential oils are sometimes ingested, but that should only be done with the guidance of your personal medical professionals. Most readily available essential oils are <u>not</u> meant to be taken internally, and those that are made for ingestion can be dangerous if you take too much.

More commonly, essential oils are used in these ways:

- Inhaled directly from the bottle or absorbent material (such as porous stones placed into bracelets, or necklaces with absorbent felt pads) or diffused into the air using misting diffusers so that you smell them

- Added to a bath or applied to your skin with a carrier oil so they can be both absorbed and smelled

Using essential oils. If you choose to experiment with using essential oils to calm anxiety and help you be more stress resilient, check off which oils you try, and write about the results you notice.

62. 4-7-8 Breathing

Anxious, stressed breathing is often shallow breathing. If you are anxious or tense for months or years, a shallow breathing pattern can result in a tense, tight diaphragm. Then the tight diaphragm further restricts your ability to take deep breaths.

Breathing exercises designed to strengthen your diaphragm and increase its elasticity also help reset your nervous system to a relaxed state and slow your heart rate. They can provide an immediate relaxed feeling, and accumulative stress-resilience benefits from routine use. *4-7-8 Breathing* is an example of such an exercise.

Based on ancient yoga practices, 4-7-8 Breathing was popularized by Integrative Medicine specialist Dr. Andrew Weil. He refers to the technique as a "natural tranquilizer for the nervous system."

Here's how 4-7-8 Breathing works

To begin, exhale to expel all the air in your lungs to start a fresh cycle of breathing.

Touch your tongue to the roof of your mouth just behind your top teeth, and leave it there for the whole exercise. Then:

The 4: close your mouth and quietly breathe in through your nose to a count of 4

The 7: hold your breath for a count of 7

The 8: exhale through your mouth for a count of 8 (allow your breath to make sound as it comes out)

Repeat the 4-7-8 steps for a total of 3 or 4 cycles.

Tips

You can do this breathing exercise standing, sitting, or lying down. Dr. Weil suggests a goal of twice daily, but once a day is better than none.

If your diaphragm is tight, or even just to get used to the breathing method, you may need to start with shorter counts than the 4, 7, and 8. Some people feel light-headed with their first attempts. Don't push yourself. Listen to your body. Work your way toward slow, relaxed breaths. This isn't meant to create stress over doing it "right."

4-7-8 Practice

Give 4-7-8 Breathing a try now
and think through your day to assess where you have a few minutes to fit it in as a routine.

63. Mindfulness

There's been lots of talk about mindfulness in the past several years.

Mindfulness is about being fully present in the current moment in a non-judgmental, curious way. That's the opposite of what's happening for most people who are anxious or worried. Anxiety and worry tend to hijack your mind and keep you fixated and ruminating on how something "awful" happened in the past or the potential of "awful" things happening in the future.

Mindfulness as you are going about your day involves:

- reminding yourself to be in the moment,
- noticing, enjoying, and savoring the feel-good, and also
- noticing, allowing, and identifying emotional discomfort.

Practicing mindfulness can help you retrain your brain to be in the here and now, so you can be less wound up and get the most out of the moment you're in. It can also help train your brain to be better able to stop intrusive thoughts or ruminating, and lower anxiety down to concern so you can logically think through options.

Below are several mindfulness exercises. If your mind wanders off while doing these exercises, gently bring it back to focused attention on the activity.

Mindful walking

You can do this exercise anywhere: in your living room, walking down a hall or in a parking lot, or outdoors when you're getting some exercise in nature. As you walk, focus your attention on the experience.

1. Notice your body's movements and the physical sensations of walking. Pay attention to:
   - The general sensation of walking
   - The movement of your feet, legs, arms, hands, abdomen, chest, neck, and head
   - Your breath

2. Take in your surroundings. Notice:
   - The sights, sounds, and smells
   - What it feels like physically (e.g., the sun or breeze on your skin)
   - What it feels like emotionally

Mindful eating

1. Get a piece of fruit (e.g., an apple, orange, or raisin).

2. Really examine the fruit. Hold it in your hand, noticing the details of what it looks like and feels like. Smell it. If it's a fruit that requires peeling, peel it slowly. Pay attention to the action of peeling it and the associated sights, sounds, and smells.

3. Slowly eat the fruit. With each bite, notice the flavor, smells, and texture.

5-4-3-2-1

This exercise involves your 5 senses: sight, touch, sound, smell, and taste.

1. Take a couple of slow, deep breaths.

2. Name 5 things you see.

3. Name 4 things you feel (e.g., the floor under your feet, warmth or cold on your skin, the clothes on your body, or something you can touch/hold).

4. Name 3 sounds you hear.

5. Name 2 things you smell.

6. Name 1 thing you taste.

7. Take a couple of slow, deep breaths.

I find it challenging to remember the sequence of this exercise, so I created this graphic to help:

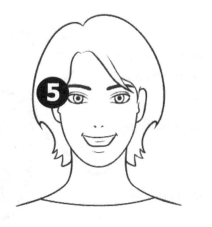  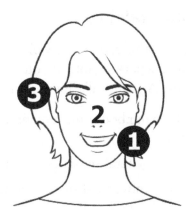

Mindfulness Practice

Pick a mindfulness exercise to give a try. You can use your favorite(s) daily to help retrain your brain to be more in the moment.

Also: Work on catching yourself not being mindful throughout your day, and pull your mind back to the here and now.

---

64. Meditation

Meditation quiets your busy conscious mind and allows you to get in touch with your subconscious mind. It is calming and relaxing. It makes room for personal insights. Making time for meditation (even a few minutes) in your daily routine may lower your overall anxiety and increase your stress resilience.

There are many different forms of meditation. The mindfulness exercises in the previous chapter are often described as meditations. Guided visualizations (like the one I suggested on page 101 for practicing relaxation skills) are a form of meditation that includes suggestions that take you on a mental journey. Some forms of meditation involve focusing on a word, phrase, or quote. Some involve focusing your eyes on an object. Some focus on relaxing parts of your body in a sequence. Some simply focus on not focusing.

Simple beginner meditation

This is a simple meditation that focuses on your breath.

1. Sit or lie down in a comfortable position. You can use the traditional meditation position if you like, but it isn't necessary.

2. Close your eyes.

3. Without trying to control your breath, notice your breath. Notice what's happening in your chest, shoulders, ribs, and abdomen as you breathe in and out.

4. If your mind wanders, that's OK. It's expected. Just gently bring it back to focusing on your breath.

5. When you're ready to end the meditation, open your eyes, mentally bring yourself back to the room. Smile.

Aim to do this meditation for a few minutes initially. You can work your way up to longer sessions if, and when, you like.

Releasing visualization

You can do a visualization meditation to release current or stored emotional pain. Do the simple beginner mediation as described above with these additions during the meditation:

- Ask yourself where in your body you feel emotional tension. Imagine you can look in your body to where the emotion is stored and notice what you see. (It could be anything: a color, a bowling ball, a bundle of wires . . . anything.) You may only feel it. That's OK too.

- Check out whether you can release some or all of it. The goal is to keep that part of the emotion that gives you wisdom and understanding, and let go of the burden part. You might see it released all at once, broken down, or dissipated. You might see or feel it flow out of your feet or hands. Experiment to see what works for you.

Loving-Kindness Meditation

Loving-kindness meditation, also known as Metta, is based on ancient traditions. It appears in different variations, but the intention and basic simplicity are consistent across the various forms. It has the potential of relieving your stress, calming your anxiety, and lifting you up in everyday situations and in challenging times.

The loving-kindness meditation consists primarily of connecting to the intention of wishing ourselves, and possibly others, safety, happiness, health, and calm.

Sit comfortably, close your eyes, take a couple of slow, deep breaths, and then begin to say the phrases listed below slowly in your mind. It may be helpful to intentionally take a breath before and/or after each phrase.

Express compassion toward yourself by slowly saying these four phrases in your mind:

- May I be safe.
- May I be happy.
- May I be healthy.
- May my mind be at ease.

Repeat the sequence as often as you like.

After the phrases that are focused on nurturing yourself, you may want to turn your focus onto other people and switch the phrases to "you" versions.

Visualize individuals or groups of people and think these phrases:

- May you be safe.
- May you be happy.
- May you be healthy.
- May your mind be at ease.

You might want to think of family, friends, co-workers, first-responders, teachers, people you like, and even people you don't like. Repeat the phrases as many times as you want regarding as many people as you want.

Meditation Practice

Pick a meditation exercise to try.
You can use one of the meditations I describe in this section or another one.

Consider working meditation into your daily routine.

---

65. More Calming Activities

Here's a list of 15 other activities that you can do on a regular basis to build your stress resilience or use to relax when you feel anxious, nervous, or worried.

1. Spend time in nature

Twenty to thirty minutes of being in nature (even just sitting in a nature setting in the middle of a city) has been shown to reduce stress and anxiety. Taking a walk outside where there are some elements of nature, or working in a garden, gives you the anti-anxiety double dip of nature exposure and exercise.

2. Take a magnesium bath or footbath

Magnesium helps relax both your body and mind. Epsom salts (magnesium sulfate) or magnesium chloride flakes can be added to a relaxing full-body bath or footbath. I find magnesium chloride flakes more powerful than Epsom salts for this. Add about one cup to a dishpan/basin of ankle-deep warm water and soak your feet for at least 20 minutes. Doing this before bed also improves sleep.

Adding calming essential oils to the bath may give your anti-stress efforts an even bigger boost in effectiveness. (See Chapter 61.)

3. Smile ☺

You don't have to be happy to smile. You can smile to be happy. Research shows that smiling releases feel-good endorphins and lowers stress-related cortisol even when it isn't a spontaneous smile.

Try it: smile for 15 seconds. See how it feels.

I call these *bonus smiles*. Work one to three bonus smiles into your day (e.g., when you first wake up, while doing the dishes, driving, waiting in line, walking from room to room . . .).

4. Write in a journal

Multiple studies have found that journaling improves both mental and physical health when it includes 3 key components: emotions, thoughts, and insights.

When all three components are present in journaling about either positive or negative experiences, writers tend to improve physically and psychologically, as indicated by less illness, less stress, less depression, better grades, and other markers of well-being. The journaling pages in this workbook were created with this research in mind. (Check out the *Also from Ann Silvers* page at the front of the workbook for more of my journals to guide you through the process.)

5. Spend time with animals

Spending time with pets can lower blood pressure, increase serotonin and dopamine (feel-good neurotransmitters), and relieve stress. Pets can help bring out your playfulness, motivate you to exercise, and provide companionship. The simple act of petting animals can be calming and soothing, creating a sense of comfort and tranquility in your daily life.

6. Listen to relaxing music

Listening to music can alter your brainwaves, so choose what you listen to wisely. Some music is relaxing, and some will rev you up. There are lots of music recordings that have been created specifically to help calm your mind. You may find them helpful, or you may prefer to experiment with the work of musicians that you enjoy to discover those pieces that are calming.

> "We may be sitting on one of the most widely available and cost-effective therapeutic modalities that ever existed. Systematically, this could be like taking a pill. Listening to music seems to be able to change brain functioning to the same extent as medication, in many circumstances." —Gabe Turow, Co-author of *Music, Science, and the Rhythmic Brain: Cultural and Clinical Implications*.

7. Listen to hypnosis recordings

Hypnosis and guided meditation recordings are extremely well suited to help with stress and anxiety because they are based on helping you relax.

I've used hypnosis as one of my tools to help reduce my clients' anxiety for decades. Through the years, I've written and rewritten hypnosis scripts for a variety of issues, including anxiety. I've used these scripts as a basis for recordings that are available for download. You can listen to the recordings any time you have a half-hour to relax or as you are going to sleep. (People often report that listening to the recordings at bedtime helps them go to sleep more easily and get a better sleep.)

A couple of recordings that you may find helpful: *Release and Refresh Emotional Detox Hypnosis* and *Discover Calm Anti-Anxiety Hypnosis*. (Available at annsilvers.com.)

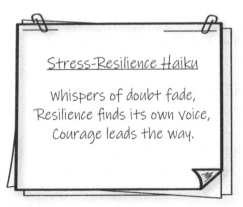

Stress-Resilience Haiku

Whispers of doubt fade,
Resilience finds its own voice,
Courage leads the way.

8. Read something inspiring

Positive novels, biographies, self-help books, blog posts, quotes, and poems can lift you up, inspire and encourage you, and help you learn how to build the skill of resilience by example or explanation.

Check out the *Maybe It's Good, Maybe It's Bad* parable on pages 184-5 and the hidden message on p. 195.

9. Play

Play is doing something for the fun of it. It's being present in the moment and savoring the joy of it. It reduces stress, releases feel-good endorphins, and helps get your brain in a creative problem-solving state. Play could involve individual activities or playing with your partner, friends, kids, or pets.

Examples of play activities: participating in sports on your own or as part of a team, flying a kite, witty banter, video or card games, Sudoku or crossword puzzles, dancing, laughing, crafts, hobbies, singing or playing a musical instrument, and blowing bubbles.

(Part Eight, coming up in a few pages, provides some word puzzles and other activities.)

10. Watch something (TV, movie, videos) that makes you laugh or smile

Remember that you have the same emotional response to something you vividly imagine as you do to something that actually happens. Anxious ruminating on awful stuff can take you down. Watching movies, TV shows, and videos that make you laugh or smile can lift you up. It's a way of using this power for your benefit instead of detriment.

11. Talk to someone supportive

You may want to set up an appointment with a therapist for some personalized help. In the next chapter, I'll walk you through different approaches to therapy that may be useful.

You might also benefit from talking with people around you. Talking to supportive family members or friends can help lift the stressed feeling, help you process stressors, and give you a boost of stress-countering joy. Having said that, not everyone has supportive family, and not all friends are supportive. You may want to pick one or a few people that you open up to.

If you aren't accustomed to reaching out to people, it doesn't have to be an all-or-nothing endeavor. You can experiment by letting people in a bit to discover who you can trust to be valuable. It may help to be clear with your support system about what you would like from them: tell them how they can help. (For example, saying something like, "I just want to vent about this. I'm not looking for solutions," if that's what you're looking for. Or, "Can I call you when I'm feeling panicky even if it's in the middle of the night?" if that's what you're looking for.)

12. Fidget with fidget jewelry and toys

Having something to fidget with may relieve your stress. There are many options in fidget rings, necklaces, bracelets, spinners, desk toys, and kids' toys. These items are designed in a form that is easy to rotate or so that an element, such as a bead or separate band, can be spun and played with. I have a client who has been wearing fidget spinner rings for years and swears by them for stress relief. She likes wearing the spinner ring on the finger next to her thumb for easy spinning.

13. Get Hot

The use of heat and sweat for health, well-being, and ceremony goes back thousands of years in many cultures across the globe. Recent research is putting scientific backing behind these traditional practices and the modern use of saunas for reducing stress and improving health and mood.

> "I'm a sauna enthusiast, and I often recommend 'sweat bathing' in saunas (or steam rooms) to cleanse the skin, soothe sore muscles, or simply relax. . . In addition to the sauna's effects on the body, many people find that it increases energy levels, reduces stress, and promotes restful sleep." —Dr. Andrew Weil, MD

14. Look at fractal patterns

Fractals are repeating patterns that recur on smaller and smaller scales. They are found in nature (shells, flowers, leaves, the rings of an onion), architecture, and art (e.g., mandalas, hypnotic spirals). Placing items with these patterns in your environment may help you relax. It can also be fun to be on the look-out for them.

> "Viewing mid-range fractals reduces your physiological response to stress by up to 60%." —R. P. Taylor, Professor of Physics, Psychology and Art, University of Oregon

15. Do some art

You don't have to be a great artist to enjoy the stress-relieving benefits of art activities. This category of adventures includes painting, scrapbooking, quilting, doodling, photography, collaging, drawing, pottery . . . and the currently very popular activity of coloring.

Drawing and coloring fractal patterns, such as mandalas, offers two stress-reducing activities at once. I included mandalas for coloring in Part Eight: Calming Activity Pages.

66. Anxiety Relief Therapies

There are many psychotherapy models that have potential for providing anxiety relief to clients. Different therapists may use a certain technique mainly or exclusively. Others—like myself—prefer to take an eclectic approach that utilizes a number of therapeutic methods.

Working one-on-one with a therapist can allow for individualized care that addresses your particular needs.

This is a partial list of therapies that may be helpful:

- **Talk Therapy** is a catch-all term for a variety of words-based therapies. In its simplest form, it offers support and guidance.

- **Psychoeducation** provides information and skills training.

- **Bibliotherapy** uses books and workbooks (like this one) to aid change. Therapists will often make suggestions along these lines to keep therapy going between sessions.

- **Cognitive Behavioral Therapy (CBT)** is based on the core concept that thoughts, feelings, and behaviors are interconnected.

- **Psychodynamic Therapy** aims to address and change the negative impact that the client's past has on their current and future thoughts, feelings, and behaviors.

- **Exposure Therapy** assists clients to systematically confront objects of their fears and phobias.

- **Eye Movement Desensitization and Reprocessing (EMDR)** uses bilateral stimulation (e.g., side-to-side eye movement) during the recall of traumatic memories to better integrate the experiences and reduce the emotional load associated with the memories.

- **Emotional Freedom Technique (EFT)** uses light tapping or touch of acupressure points to relieve emotional distress from current and past experiences. (The therapist doesn't touch the client. It's more like a call-and-repeat sequence.)

- **Mindfulness-Based Therapy** utilizes mindfulness and meditative practices as change agents.

- **Hypnotherapy** uses hypnosis specifically for therapeutic purposes. It helps you relax, much like in guided meditation or visualization, or yoga relaxation techniques. It gets past the busy conscious mind and accesses your subconscious to undo harm from experiences, reinforce new ways of being, and affect positive change.

- **Integrative Medicine for Mental Health** looks at both the body and mind. It integrates psychological theories together with knowledge about how physical processes, nutrition, and lifestyle impact mood.

Other therapies that can help relieve stress and anxiety include:

- acupuncture, massage therapy, and biofeedback.

67. Stress Resilience Lifestyle Summary

1. Modifications to sleep and exercise routines, as well as alcohol and caffeine intake, can reduce anxiety and increase stress resilience.

2. General advice for anti-stress eating is the same basic advice given for healthy eating:

    1. Focus on real food

    2. Eat protein throughout the day

    3. Eat your vegetables

    4. Have some fruit but don't overdo it

    5. Eat a variety of foods

    6. Drink enough water

3. **10 Stress Resilience Supplements:** Magnesium • B vitamins • Vitamin C • Vitamin D$_3$ • Omega-3 Fats, EPA and DHA • Probiotics • Adaptogens (e.g., Ashwagandha, Maca Root, Holy Basil, Rhodiola, Schisandra, and American ginseng) • L-Theanine • Zinc • Nervine herbs (e.g., Chamomile, Valerian, Passionflower, and Lemongrass)

4. **Calming essential oils include:** Lavender • Lemongrass • Sweet orange • Geranium • Bergamot • Ylang Ylang • Lemon balm • Bitter orange, AKA neroli • Rose

5. To increase your stress resilience and reduce anxiety, you could:

    • Practice 4-7-8 breathing, mindfulness, or meditation

    • Spend time in nature

    • Take a magnesium bath

    • Smile

    • Journal

    • Spend time with animals

    • Listen to relaxing music or hypnosis recordings

    • Read something inspiring

    • Play

    • Watch something that makes you laugh or smile

    • Talk to someone supportive (friend, family, therapist)

    • Fidget with fidget jewelry and toys

    • Get hot

    • Look at fractal patterns

    • Do some art

Part Eight

Calming Activity Pages

This section contains an inspiring story,
some coloring pages using fractal patterns,
and a few other activities for learning, fun, and inspiration.

Use any of the pages that are interesting to you.

There are blank pages behind coloring pages in case you would like to use markers
that might bleed through. You may want to place a blank sheet of paper behind the
page you're coloring on for extra protection.

Answers to the puzzles are on page 200.

Discover the Message

Fill in the word shapes from the word list to discover the message.
(Not all the words listed are answers. Some words are used more than once.)

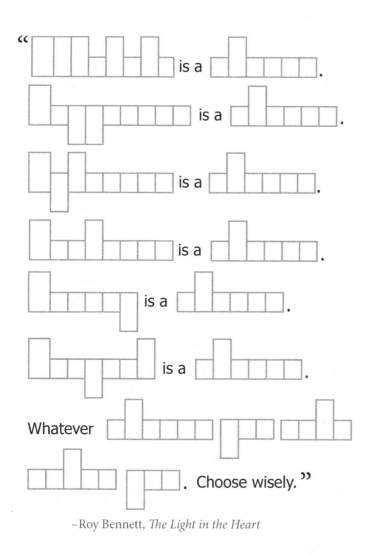

–Roy Bennett, *The Light in the Heart*

Thought
Happiness
possibility
Smiling
takes
Kindness
make
Sadness
art
Opportunity
you
Respect
decision
makes
option
strength
Giving
choice
Attitude
possibility
Pessimism
skill
Optimism
take
Gratitude

Maybe It's Good. Maybe It's Bad

Here is my version of the Chinese Farmer parable or fable that can help you pull out of awfulizing or catastrophizing about your life.

A farmer who was feeling down and out because his farm was not doing well went to the local guru to complain about his plight and seek advice. The guru's response to his story: "Maybe it's good. Maybe it's bad."

The farmer found the guru's surprising "advice" disappointing and confusing. He tossed and turned that night, unable to sleep for worry about his situation. His head spun, imagining his family's awful future.

When the farmer woke in the morning, he was shocked to see that a wild horse had entered his yard. The horse was an impressive strong stallion that he could harness and use to work the fields. Ecstatic, the farmer ran to tell the guru about his good fortune. The guru's response to his story: "Maybe it's good. Maybe it's bad." "Wow," the farmer thought. "That was unexpected."

The farmer invested all the money he had left in seeds. He planted his seeds with the help of the horse. Spring turned into summer and fall. Just as it was time to bring in the harvest, the farmer woke one morning to find that the horse had run away.

The farmer was despondent. He had spent all his money on seeds, nurtured the plants all summer, and now couldn't see how he would be able to bring in the harvest. Feeling anxious and overwhelmed, the farmer returned to the guru. After listening to the story, the guru simply said, "Maybe it's good. Maybe it's bad." "This can't be good!" thought the farmer.

The next day, the stallion returned and brought with him a mare. Now the farmer had two horses to help bring in the crops and would be able to have horses into the future as the pair produced offspring. The farmer excitedly told the guru this wonderful news. The guru's response: "Maybe it's good. Maybe it's bad."

The next day, the farmer's son was riding the stallion while helping with the harvest. The son was bucked off the horse and sustained injuries that would incapacitate him for months. Overcome with grief and worry, the farmer returned to the guru. Again, the guru said, "Maybe it's good. Maybe it's bad." "Really, how could this be good?" thought the farmer.

The next week, army recruiters came to town. The country was at war, and all able-bodied young men were taken off to fight at the front lines. The son's injuries saved him from having to go off to fight.

Maybe it's good. Maybe it's bad. Maybe it's somewhere in between. Maybe it's some of both.

Rather than think of events as being absolutely good or absolutely bad, consider a continuum of outcomes. On one far end of the continuum is "absolutely entirely wonderful" and on the other end of the continuum is "absolutely entirely awful."

Each event can be placed somewhere on the continuum. The combination of good and bad will determine where on the continuum it belongs.

If you find yourself dwelling on awful possibilities (awfulizing), it may be helpful to think of the guru's words. "Maybe it's good. Maybe it's bad."

The slogan may help snap you out of awfulizing and help you de-stress.

You don't know where the twists and turns of life will take you until the future plays out. Sometimes, events that seem awful turn out to contain something wonderful (or at least something somewhat good).

Have you had an experience in your past when you felt despondent about a situation and later realized that some good came out of it? You can use that experience to inspire you through your next challenge. Remember, "Maybe it's good. Maybe it's bad," and smile.

189

Breathe. Relax. Smile.

There's More Than One Way

There's more than one way to get where you want to be.

Emotions Word Search

```
M R R G D E T C E T O R P W
C L V N E Y L U F E P O H R
M V L P M N K M B D H P K N
Q T Y G P X R Z O A X N R P
P D R K O Z R O P G N D K P
J L T H W W T P Q R M E L G
L T H T E S Y Y N A J T B D
N D L D R R K D H T D P P E
B K E E E C O M P E T E N T
P L D L D D P P R F H C M S
M N M J I L U U M U V C X U
U D Y W Q G S L B L M A W R
B E K H B S H J C Y P M Y T
B V Y K A X N T G N L L N W
G O S E C U R E E A I D J R
M L R M N V M Z C D T M N T
```

Find these words. (Words can be forwards, backwards, up, down, or diagonal.)

ACCEPTED	GRATEFUL	PROTECTED
CALM	HAPPY	REASSURED
COMPETENT	HOPEFUL	SECURE
DELIGHTED	INCLUDED	TRUSTED
EMPOWERED	LOVED	UNDERSTOOD

Discover the Message

Unscramble the emotion words and enter letters from the unscrambled words into the number-corresponding boxes in the message. (The words are from the comfortable emotions word list.)

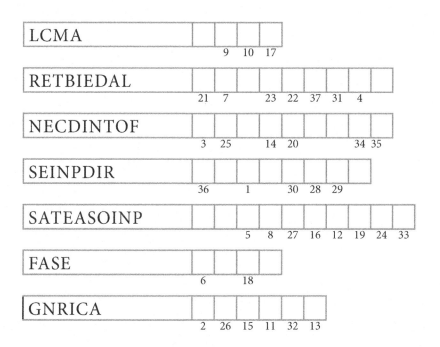

LCMA — _ _ _ _ (9 10 17)

RETBIEDAL — _ _ _ _ _ _ _ _ (21 7 _ 23 22 37 31 4)

NECDINTOF — _ _ _ _ _ _ _ _ _ (3 25 _ 14 20 _ _ 34 35)

SEINPDIR — _ _ _ _ _ _ _ (36 1 _ 30 28 29)

SATEASOINP — _ _ _ _ _ _ _ _ _ (5 8 27 16 12 19 24 33)

FASE — _ _ _ _ (6 _ 18)

GNRICA — _ _ _ _ _ _ (2 26 15 11 32 13)

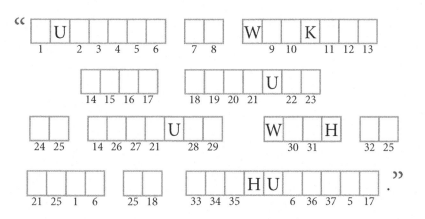

" _ [U] _ _ _ _   _ _ [W] _ [K] _ _ _
  1 2 3 4 5 6   7 8 9 10 11 12 13

_ _ _ _   _ _ _ _ [U] _ _
14 15 16 17 18 19 20 21 22 23

_ _   _ _ _ [U] _ _   [W] _ [H]   _ _
24 25 14 26 27 21 28 29 30 31 32 25

_ _ _ _   _ _   _ _ _ [H][U] _ _ _ _ "
21 25 1 6 25 18 33 34 35 6 36 37 5 17 .

-Winston Churchill

Word List
- ☐ Accepted
- ☐ Acknowledged
- ☐ Amused
- ☐ Appreciated
- ☐ Attracted
- ☐ Attractive
- ☐ Calm
- ☐ Capable
- ☐ Caring
- ☐ Competent
- ☐ Confident
- ☐ Connected
- ☐ Considered
- ☐ Content
- ☐ Creative
- ☐ Curious
- ☐ Delighted
- ☐ Empowered
- ☐ Encouraged
- ☐ Enthusiastic
- ☐ Excited
- ☐ Exhilarated
- ☐ Grateful
- ☐ Happy
- ☐ Hopeful
- ☐ Important
- ☐ Included
- ☐ Independent
- ☐ Inspired
- ☐ Interested
- ☐ Liberated
- ☐ Loved
- ☐ Nurtured
- ☐ Passionate
- ☐ Protected
- ☐ Proud
- ☐ Reassured
- ☐ Relaxed
- ☐ Relieved
- ☐ Respected
- ☐ Safe
- ☐ Satisfied
- ☐ Secure
- ☐ Stimulated
- ☐ Supported
- ☐ Surprised
- ☐ Trusted
- ☐ Trusting
- ☐ Understood
- ☐ Valued
- ☐ Welcome 195

About the Author

Ann Silvers, MA
Counselor, Relationship Coach,
Hypnotherapist and Author

I haven't always been a counselor. During my first career, I was a Medical Lab Tech working in Microbiology labs in a couple of large hospitals in Canada. When I was pregnant with my first child, I dove into learning everything I could about parenting because I didn't want to parent the way I was parented. (I was raised by two alcoholics.) A big part of my learning focused on communication and emotion skills.

When my children were young, two things happened that set my course toward a counseling career: I was invited to teach a local counselor's parenting class, and I had therapy to deal with my childhood. I decided that when I was ready to return to the paid workforce, I wanted to work with humans, not microorganisms. I wanted to help other people experience the positive changes I felt from my therapy and self-help discoveries.

So—while I took advantage of opportunities to teach communication and relationship skills workshops, I went back to school to get degrees in psychology and counseling. (By that time, I had moved with my family to the Seattle area in the US.)

Over decades of working with people in groups, and as individuals and couples, I developed ways of explaining concepts and created exercise materials that I eventually turned into card sets, books, and recordings for publication, so that more people could benefit from the products that are the result of years of experimenting with using and improving.

You can find me on social media and annsilvers.com (eStore and blog).

One Last Thing

If you liked *Becoming Calm: Silver Lining Anxiety and Stress Resilience Workbook and Journal* and found it helpful, please leave a review on Amazon. Every 5-star review helps other people find the workbook and reap the benefits of using it.

If you have concerns about the book, please contact me so I can make improvements to the workbook for future users: ann@annsilvers.com.

Thank you so much.

Wishing you health, happiness & prosperity,

-Ann Silvers

Activity Pages Answers

Page 183

"Attitude is a choice.
Happiness is a choice.
Optimism is a choice.
Kindness is a choice.
Giving is a choice.
Respect is a choice.
Whatever choice you make
makes you. Choose wisely."
-Roy T. Bennett,
The Light in the Heart

Page 194

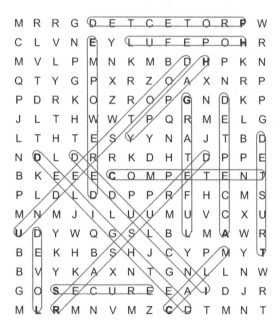

Page 195

CALM
LIBERATED
CONFIDENT
INSPIRED
PASSIONATE
SAFE
CARING

"Success is walking from
failure to failure with
no loss of enthusiasm."
—Winston Churchill

Additional Reflections

"I want to write about me,
my discoveries, my fears, my feelings, about me."

—Helen Keller

Made in the USA
Monee, IL
08 January 2024